The Ties That Bind
Ending a Generational Curse of Betrayal, Abuse & Trauma

ANNETTE COPELAND

ISBN: PENDING

1st Edition

DEDICATION

This book is dedicated to all of the women and men who have stood in their power to challenge and break generational patterns of toxicity and abuse so that the next generation of humans can live happy, safe and fulfilled lives and to my granddaughters who deserve to live the best possible lives full of joy and balance.

DISCLAIMER

THIS BOOK IS A SECOND EDITION OF
DRAGONFLY INTO THE LIGHT
INCLUDING ADDITIONAL CHAPTERS

5 Stars "The book is amazing. So eye opening and relatable. It's a must read for men and women to get into the mind of an abused individual and understand the healing process." **Roxanne G.**

5 Stars "I really enjoyed this book. I finished within a few hours I had to see how it ended!! A lot of folks can relate to this book. Really liked how the author gave the number and website to get help for abuse." **Baummm**

5 Stars "I enjoyed the book and freely recommend it. The main characters were easy to relate to and I was drawn into their story which flowed smoothly from the first page to the last. Which is good because it's a "read it cover-to-cover" in one sitting. The story contains suspense, a little romance, and a great deal of insight into relationships, good and bad." **Angelique G.**

5 Stars "I usually do not read books but when I received this one I could not put it down! I started it in the evening and finished the next morning! A little suspense and love! You felt connected to Shari and how she went through this experience and how to learn to overcome it! A must read!" **Jill K**

5 Stars "Very Good Book. It was a very good book. Readers will love this." **Connie L**

5 Stars "WOW Great Read! A Must Buy! When you finish reading a book and you cry tears, you know you have found something special. This is a book about a woman who is overcoming a troubled relationship with emotional abuse and follows her journey as she finds strength, peace and love again.

You learn that by reading this book you are not alone. You were never alone, you just never knew it. You now feel validated and that you can actually recover and find peace and happiness again.

If you know someone who has lived in abuse, which could be any form, this book is for them...or, if someone you think may be in an abusive relationship, this would be a good way to help them; buy this book for them. Easy to read in a story line format with the gems of wisdom and help as you read through the protagonist's journey." **Stasia**

5 Stars "Keeps you focused and interested, while learning we can all overcome trauma. Anonymous

5 Stars "Amazing! I loved it. You won't want to put it down after you start reading." **Anonymous**

5 Stars "Very Captivating. Great Book. I read it in two days!" **Anonymous**

INTRODUCTION

Shari was startled, but she didn't dare open her eyes. She lay there, paralyzed, listening to every sound in the room. She was struggling to understand why she was suddenly awake and afraid. Had he found her? Was he in the house? She could feel her heart pounding and between every heartbeat she could hear the blood rushing through her veins. *Boom, swish, boom-boom, swish.* She was afraid to open her eyes but she was more afraid to keep them shut. She slowly opened her eyes just a tiny slit and saw that the room was still dark.

There were no shadows hovering above her, so she opened her eyes further and slowly scanned the room, lying perfectly still. Her heart was racing and even though she saw nothing out of the ordinary in the room, she was gripped in the clutches of fear. Her stomach twisted into a knot, and an uneasy feeling was slowly working its way up her chest.

She listened carefully, waiting to hear someone breathing but didn't. She flipped off the blankets and lurched toward the light switch on the wall, blasting the room with bright light. She stood there holding her nightgown tightly against her body, waiting for what was going to happen next. Her imagination was running wild and she thought at any moment he was going to step out of the dark with that sneer on his face that she had grown to hate.

She felt hot tears welling up in her eyes and even though she had trained herself to hold back emotions, her eyes failed her and one single tear slowly ran down her cheek and fell silently to the hardwood floor. Straightening her spine and pushing her shoulders back, she angrily wiped her face with the back of her tightly closed fist and took a step toward the closed door. Keenly aware of her surroundings, she scanned the room one more time and saw nothing out of place. She quickly grabbed her robe from the hook on the back of the bedroom door, wrapped herself in its comfortable embrace and slowly made her way down the dark hallway. She needed to see if there was anything out of place in the house. Turning on every light switch as she walked silently but purposefully toward the kitchen, she saw it.

The broom was lying on the floor near the back door. Glancing at the locked deadbolt, she thought, "That must be it. The stupid broom." She released the breath she had been holding. Then she said out loud to herself, "Great! No sleep for me tonight." Her best friend, Lily, must have slept right through the ruckus because she heard nothing but the whir of a fan coming from behind the closed door to her bedroom. She was safe, for now.

She methodically checked each window and door to make sure they were latched and locked tight before filling a glass with water and heading back down the hallway to her room. There would be little sleep tonight. Only memories of a time she would rather forget but her mind would not allow. She recognized the all-too-familiar feelings of anxiety creeping into her mind. She could see her heart beating through her robe and her stomach was in knots.

Her throat felt tightly closed off and she thought she was never going to be able to close her eyes, let alone feel safe enough to sleep. Shari propped herself up on her bed, pulled the blankets up tight and turned on the TV, searching for something to keep her mind busy.

She had been free of his control for months but she still blamed herself for staying in the relationship long past the now obvious expiration date. How had she missed the signs of crazy-making in the beginning? How did she not see his behavior as odd, desperate and controlling? How did she not see herself changing to accommodate his moods? She was thankful that her best friend, Lily, had an extra bedroom and was perfectly content having her as a roommate but she felt like no one, not even her best friend, would understand her reasons for not wanting to live alone.

She had left in such a hurry with only her clothing and a few personal belongings. It was so much easier to stay with Lily than to find her own place right now. She lost her grandmother's china cabinet, her photo albums from high school and so many little things she could never replace but it was too painful to go back and ask for them now. She never wanted to see or speak to him again. She could hear him telling everyone it was his grandmother's china cabinet and saying that she lied anyway. He could be so convincing.

She looked back on past relationships and realized that she had never had to run away in a rush or give up her personal possessions before. Of course, no breakup is easy, but she had always been able to have a reasonable conversation with her exes and it was never an issue to transfer personal property that had been inadvertently overlooked. This time was different. She was afraid—more afraid than she had ever been.

She was thankful for her lifelong friends and the life that was still waiting for her when she returned, but she felt like an observer in her own life. She was outside looking in and she felt like she could not trust her own intuition or decision-making skills any longer. She feared commitment and refused to even join the local gym because she could not agree to the monthly payment. She remembered how she was before him. She was happy, active and social. She had her own apartment and was saving to buy a house.

That wasn't possible now because her savings had been drained. The future life she had planned long before she met him had been tainted and now seemed lost because he

9

had inserted himself into her future plans so perfectly that it was hard to imagine wanting to do those things anymore.

She was confused and angry but glad to be safe in this small bedroom with her dear friend just down the hall. She leaned back and rested her head on a big fluffy pillow and focused on a time when life was easy and free. She wondered if she could ever feel that way again. The TV droned in the background as she focused on slowing her breathing and heart rate and silently drifted off to sleep.

The Ties That Bind
Ending a Generational Curse of Betrayal, Abuse & Trauma

The Ties That Bind

1 DRAGONFLY

Shari slipped back into reality as the dragonfly buzzed past her ear. For a moment, she almost forgot about the events of the past year. It had been a few days since the terrifying broom incident and she was doing her best to stay in the moment.

The sun beating down on her tanned skin, covered simply by a small red and white bikini, was hot, even though the temperature was only seventy-five or so. She watched several brightly colored blue dragonflies dart around carelessly, and thought about how good it felt to be there. Slowly and purposefully she brushed away the beautiful, large-eyed creature that had perched on her knee for a second, and completed the task of applying her suntan lotion.

The light breeze and smell of coconut made her feel far away from the rocky beach where she had spent so many summer afternoons since…since that day. No, she wouldn't think about it or him. She shook off the image in her head and tried to focus on a distant cloud. She chuckled to herself, thinking it looked a bit like a dragon or some sort of mythical beast.

She thought back and tried to focus on her summer. She wondered why she spent so much time here. It was nothing special, just a small rocky beach in a shallow part of the stream, not even deep enough to swim in. She dipped her left foot into the water just under her carefully placed lounge chair. It felt good on her hot skin. She was alone on the beach today, except for the dragonflies or an occasional bird squawking in the distance.

During the hottest part of the summer there would be other sunbathers and families roasting hot dogs over an open fire on the gravel bar. Children would run and splash in the cool spring-fed water. Even in August when the sun was hottest, the water would always be cold. The springs kept it that way.

She decided to wade out knee-deep and cool off some. It was abnormally warm for mid-September, and the days like this would soon be gone.

"Better enjoy it while you can," her friend Lily stated as she climbed into her car. "I would come with you but my boss will kill me if I call in again!"

She laughed to herself at the memory from earlier that day; Lily was right on both counts. If she called in sick she would probably get fired. They had enjoyed so many fun days over the summer, and Lily couldn't resist a good time, so she had missed a few too many days just to go to the river or out to play. Shari felt a pang of guilt and promised herself that she would help Lily get back into good graces with Phil, her boss. He was easygoing enough, and would ultimately forgive her, but he had every reason to be upset.

Lily and Shari had met some five years before at a small gathering with mutual friends. Shari liked Lily immediately. Lily had a kind of recklessness that Shari could never really understand but admired in a way—even though sometimes Shari felt as if she was the only thing that kept Lily from doing something insane, or at least insane in her eyes.

Shari was a bit more reserved and not spontaneous at all. She preferred to plan ahead for spontaneous activities. She chuckled to herself and said out loud, "Not really spontaneous that way. Is it?"

It would be several more hours before she had Lily to keep her occupied. One blue dragonfly perched on her thigh and she watched it curiously for a minute before it darted left, then right and zoomed off into the distance. She mused at the idea that the beautiful creature was in the final stages of life but appeared to be living life to the fullest. A smile started to form on her lips as she settled back into her lounger and closed her eyes, wanting to soak up all the sun that was left for the day.

She reminded herself that Lily was a great example of how to live life to the fullest. Their personalities were so different, yet they had a lot in common and there was rarely a moment of silence when they were together. Lily was very athletic. She was good at everything that Shari was not. Shari was tall and clumsy; she always blamed it on her blonde hair, but she was just not very coordinated. She liked to joke that she could hurt herself taking a nap, but it was probably more truth than a joke. Lily loved to party, and Shari loved to hang out in crowds, she enjoyed all the people. There was a certain energy in a large group of people, and she loved running into old friends.

Shari was tall and thin, almost too thin this summer, and Lily was average height and had a beautiful, athletic build. They were about as opposite as they could be. Shari was a fair-skinned, natural blonde and had no idea how beautiful she really was. Lily was more exotic-looking with olive skin, long dark hair, and huge brown eyes. Lily was more confident—probably due to the sports she had played her whole life. Together, they made quite an entrance at a party, and party was what Lily loved to do!

That's how Shari met "him." Lily disliked him immediately, but Shari thought he was mysterious and intelligent, and oh-so smooth. For some reason she was drawn to him, probably because he didn't come right out and hit on her with some cheesy pickup line. He just started talking to her like he had known her for years and it almost seemed like he did.

He was quick with compliments and made Shari feel like the only girl in the room. It had been a while since she felt so connected to someone in such a short time, and he was deliberate to mention that they seemed like soulmates. He was so interested in what she liked and wanted out of life and his goals were so similar to hers. When he asked Shari for her number it seemed perfectly normal. They had a chemistry that made her feel attracted to him.

He promised to call her the next day, but he started texting her as soon as they left the bar. When she woke she had several unopened texts thanking her for being amazing, and the final one said: "Good morning, beautiful."

The following weeks were filled with thoughtful messages and secret calls to her office phone. He seemed to be perfect in every way. Their goals for the future were the same; they liked all of the same things. She adored the attention he gave so freely and was so excited to have finally met someone so much like her. They were like twin spirits. He reminded her that she was his soulmate often. From the stories he told her he had big plans but had always had bad luck. He just needed her to believe in him and their lives would be magical.

They started making plans for the future immediately, and even though she had a quiet voice in the back of her mind that said slow down, she raced forward into this relationship like no other. It was only a few weeks before he started moving his things into her apartment. She happily rearranged the closet and furniture to allow more space for him and the few belongings that he had. She felt so bad for him because his last girlfriend had kicked him out with no notice and would not allow him access to the house to get his things. He claimed to have a bed and a living room full of furniture but she kept it out of spite, according to him.

His calls seemed to always interrupt her workday and eventually, she would have to ask him to stop calling her at work because it was being noticed by other employees and she was afraid her boss would frown on the amount of time she spent entertaining him during work hours. He promised to be more careful and started meeting her for lunch every day instead.

At the time she thought it was sweet that he wanted to be with her so much. She literally spent every waking minute with him unless she was at work. They shopped together, exercised together, ate together and even showered and slept together. In the beginning, Shari didn't even notice that she had no personal time. It was so much fun being with him that she was fine not spending time with her family or friends and was completely overjoyed to be welcomed with open arms by his friends and family.

It wasn't long before signs of his dark side started to appear. Shari could have easily pointed them out if it had been one of her friends dating him, but because it was her, she either didn't see them or chose to ignore them. Shari always called these signs "little red flags" and commonly warned her friends by blurting out "little red flag" in the middle of a conversation with a friend. It always prompted a roar of laughter within her group of girls, which she also enjoyed. The only thing she liked more than helping her friends was making them laugh.

That's what kept her so close to "HIM"; she could tell that he needed something, some kind of help and she wanted more than anything to do that for him. He could be so caring and gentle, but he had a dark side that he kept very guarded. She only saw tiny flashes of it from time to time. She couldn't help but think that if she could get him through what was bothering him, he would make a wonderful husband someday.

He constantly told stories about his past life. They were so full of sadness and Shari was so shocked that he had such bad luck with relationships and jobs. It seemed like he always got the worst boss and was never really appreciated for what he "brought to the table." Shari could see how smart he was and saw so much potential in him and wanted to help him be successful.

She eagerly shared her dreams with him about the future. She wanted to purchase a home and live in it for a few years and then rent it out and buy a new house, then more and more. She had big plans to have several rentals and other ideas for income that would support her love of travel. Shari knew if she stayed with her current job that she would have several weeks of vacation soon and she planned to travel as much as possible.

He claimed to be excellent at fixing and flipping real estate and that he could do all of the work himself. He seemed like the perfect fit for her future plans.

He was not handsome but very average-looking. He was the same height as her, maybe even a bit shorter, but he was muscular and much stronger than he looked. He had a way of making conversation with anyone. He was never a stranger in a crowd, which she admired because she loved crowds. Shari was a bit more shy and rarely struck up a conversation with someone unless they made it clear that they were open to it.

She hoped a bit of his outgoing personality would rub off on her and make her more at ease with new people. She assumed because of his abilities he must have lots of friends, but she would find out in months to come that she was his only true friend.

His ability to strike up a conversation with someone was about as far as his skills went. If he had any friends at all it was because they pursued it, not him. He had acquaintances, and lots of them. Shari had friends, real friends, too many to count. She would learn that this was very important later on.

He was street-smart and very intelligent with an iron-clad memory, which was a vital part of his personality. This allowed him to remember what story he gave each person so as not to change it later on and she would learn he used it to remind people of the secrets they shared with him in private.

Shari had few secrets. She had done some things she was embarrassed about when she was younger, but who hadn't? She was very loyal and not a liar. She had no memory for those things, so she made a point to always tell the truth. This way she didn't have to remember what she told someone.

Her ability to be honest would eventually come back to haunt her, because he loved asking her for intimate details about her past and what he loved even more was creating a detailed list in his mind of all the ways he would use them against her if she ever double-crossed him. He made it a point to bring up things she had shared with him from her past anytime she pushed his limits, and he reminded her how ashamed she would be if he shared them with her friends or family.

He monitored her phone conversations and without her knowledge, even checked her phone periodically to see who she had been talking to when she was not with him. His constant questions while she was on the phone with her friends, whom she missed very much, made it difficult to have conversations with them. Eventually, she just stopped talking to them when he was with her, and if they called, Shari would find a reason to get off the phone. It just wasn't worth it, but she still didn't see the "little red flags."

Slowly he managed to get her all to himself, which he wanted more than anything. Without the interference of her friends he could control every move she made, and he was very proud of his accomplishment. He had her right where he wanted her, and she didn't even see it happen until it was too late.

A cool breeze interrupted her thoughts and she shivered. It was cooling off quickly, so she gathered up her things and headed for the car. Upset with herself for thinking about "him," Shari crammed her chair and towels into the trunk and slammed the lid. Climbing into the car she realized it was almost four o'clock, Lily would be off work soon. She smiled as she pulled out onto the highway. She wouldn't have to be alone anymore today.

2 SATURDAY NIGHT

As Shari pulled into the driveway her cell phone rang and she jumped. She hated that sound. Her heart immediately started pounding. After the "breakup" he had called her screaming obscenities so many times that just the sound of it ringing was enough to make her nauseous. With a shaking hand she reached deep into her purse to find the screaming phone. She saw it was Lily and quickly answered it with a sheepish, "Hello?"

"What's for dinner? I'm famished!" shouted Lily over the sound of the wind from the open car window.

"Anything but takeout!" said Shari, feeling better already. She threw the car into park and hopped out, leaving the beach equipment in the trunk. Maybe tomorrow would be as nice as today.

"Well it is Saturday," stated Lily. "We could go out on the town for a bit. You need to get out anyway. You can't stay cooped up in the house every weekend. Waddaya say?"

"Yeah, you're right, I know. I just hate to be hit on, and I am not looking for a man so it seems useless to let them all slobber all over me. Especially since most of them would marry a snake if it could do dishes."

They both let out a loud laugh, and Lily scoffed, "That's

why I love you, you have such a bright outlook on things. Anyway, if I go without you I won't have anyone to make man-hater jokes with, will I? C'mon we'll have a good time I promise."

"We always do!" stated Shari. "I think I am up for a good evening of male bashing anyway, I guess we could go out for a few drinks. See ya' when you get here!"

Shari made a dash for the shower, she could be in and out in twenty minutes, but if Lily beat her, it would be an hour before she could use their one small bathroom. Of course, she would change clothes four times before Lily was ready to go so it would work out anyway.

She wondered who would be out tonight. Maybe she would see some old friends. That would make it all worth it. She had been spending so much time at home the last few months and she had lost touch with some of her friends. It seemed like a good opportunity to see them. She was not enjoying being single this time. She was still carrying too much baggage from her recent breakup. She didn't even like the idea of meeting any new prospective dates; it actually made her sick to her stomach just thinking about it.

As she showered she thought about how perfect she had imagined her life three years ago. All she wanted was a good man, kids and a house with a white picket fence. She chuckled and said out loud, "White picket fence syndrome." She needed to reevaluate her expectations and decide what she really wanted out of life. As much as she thought she knew what she wanted, she was unsure now if she had made the right choices so far, and she was afraid of her own decision-making ability. All she really wanted was unconditional love and a solid foundation for a good life; she wondered if that was even something that existed.

She slinked to her bedroom in a towel and climbed into

her tattered cotton robe she had loved since high school. It was still the most comfortable piece of clothing she owned. She wrapped her head in a towel and was standing in front of the closet when Lily came in the door. "You alright? You sounded funny on the phone earlier. He didn't call you, did he?"

"No, he didn't, but he may as well have. Every time my phone rings I just get sick instantly. He hasn't called since that one Friday night that I didn't answer and he left me like two thousand messages. Maybe he finally got the hint."

Lily quipped, "Maybe he found some other poor unsuspecting victim and will leave you alone now! Why don't you change the ring on your phone, maybe it will change your outlook on getting phone calls. Never know, someone nice might call. You wouldn't want to sound all freaked out then would you?"

"Someone better not call me—what have you been up to? I told you I am not interested in dating," Shari said in a panicked voice.

"Oh, calm down, Shari. You know I would never give your number out without asking you first." Lily ran for the shower and shouted out through the partially open door, "Let's go eat at that new place, I heard they have a great atmosphere. I also heard that Leo hangs out there sometimes. He is a really nice guy and I think he has his eye on you!"

"Jeez, you never listen do you? I don't care if he is there or not." Shari fumbled with her phone and listened to several other ring options and finally settled on a different sound. Maybe Lily was right. It could help.

What if Leo was there? She had met him earlier this summer at a party on the Fourth of July, down at the river. It was a huge bash with upwards of one hundred people there so she was able to excuse herself quickly without making it seem like she was avoiding him. He was a handsome man, probably a couple of years older than her but he didn't look it. He was tall, rugged and tanned from his job outdoors. She wasn't sure exactly what he did for a living but she could tell he enjoyed it. At that time she was still very heartbroken and shocked over her recent breakup with "HIM"; she really was not at all interested in meeting anyone, or even talking to them for that matter.

She had only attended the "swimsuit only" party for Lily. She wanted backup and moral support. She had met a new guy and wanted Shari's opinion of him. His name was Alex. Shari could not see why Lily was so interested in him, he was good-looking but self-centered and obviously a player. That was her first and only impression of him. Their attraction didn't last long. Lily caught him in a compromising position with her little sister, of all people. He was no longer on "the list."

Shari turned her attention back to the closet. She hadn't really thought about what to wear and time was ticking. She tried on a couple of different outfits and none really seemed to be right. Too loose (no self-esteem), too tight (slutty), too long (nunish); why was this so hard? She always had trouble choosing what to wear. She remembered she had a black skirt. It was short but not too short. Where was it though? She yelled over the sound of the water in the shower. "Hey, have you seen my black skirt?"

Lily replied, "Yeah, it's on the dryer. I wore it but it's clean!" Shari went to check it out; they shared clothes often. The only thing they couldn't share was pants. Her legs were at least four inches longer than Lily's. The skirt was it. Perfect. She finished getting dressed and applied just the right amount of makeup and spent a little extra time on her hair. It was good to feel pretty. She went to the kitchen to get a glass of wine; all that was left to do now was wait for Lily to complete her hairdo and they could go. Lily saw her with the glass of wine and said, "Getting an early start, huh? Hey, that skirt looks great. I wish my legs were that long."

Shari came back with a scoff, "Yeah, and covered with scars from being a klutz? You are the lucky one, you can do anything, and I can hurt myself taking a nap."

Lily calmly stated, "That's not because of your legs, dearie, it's because you're a blonde." They both laughed and sat down at the kitchen table for a few minutes so Shari could finish her wine.

Then they hopped into the car and off they sped. It was dark already but still warm enough to have the windows down if you weren't going too fast. A song they both loved came on the radio and Lily reached over and turned the volume up loud enough they had to yell to hear each other talk. No need to talk though; singing was all they did. They laughed and snapped their fingers to the beat. It felt great to be alive. What a beautiful evening.

Once they arrived at the restaurant they chose a small booth near the bar where Lily could "keep an eye on things." They shared an appetizer and each had a lime margarita, on the rocks, no salt. When the waitress brought the check it was marked PAID. Both girls looked at each other and Lily stated, "This better not be from Alex; if he thinks that this is all it takes…" but stopped suddenly as a thin smile came across her face.

"Don't look now, but there's Leo. Do you think he did this? Hey, come here for a sec." She waved to the waitress. "Who paid our tab?" The waitress slowly leaned in and pointed toward Leo's table where he was sitting with one of his friends. Lily raised her eyebrow and whispered, "I told you he has his eye on you."

Shari, not wanting to accept that as the reason, stated,

"Oh no, he probably just figures he still owes you for saving him from spending most of his night talking to Priscilla at that dance a couple weeks ago. If you hadn't interrupted she would have kept him to herself all evening."

"Shari," said Lily, "He would not pay a thirty-dollar tab for something so trivial. He did it for you. Anyway, she is not that bad; she may be a pain but he is a grown man and he would have come up with a way to get rid of her on his own." Lily laughed out loud, louder than she would have otherwise.

"Lily, stop! Don't draw his attention." But it was too late, he was on his way to their table.

"We have to thank him don't we?" she said sarcastically.

They both watched as he and his friend approached their table. He walked so carefree—so straight and smooth, not a strut at all but with such an air of confidence. She admired him for that. He sauntered up to the edge of their table and asked, "Enjoy your dinner?"

Shari blushed under his intent gaze and Lily responded, "Yes, it was great. Thank you. Someone paid our check, was that you?"

Leo never looked her way. He just said, "Yes. Is that OK?" as if Shari was the one who had thanked him.

Shari nodded and managed to choke out, "Yes, thank you."

He asked if they were going to the club up the street to dance, and Lily couldn't resist the opportunity to get Shari and Leo in the same room. "Yep, we are headed there next. I didn't know you danced?"

Leo smiled and said, "There's a lot about me you don't know. Well, we are headed there now so I guess we'll see you there."

His friend nodded as they walked away. Lily mocked,

"That one must be mute, ya think?"

Shari laughed, and kicked Lily under the table for her blatant behavior. "Why did you tell him we were going there?"

Lily calmly stated, "Well, we are, aren't we?" She smiled a big smile knowing she had Shari just where she wanted her. Shari would have to go now, she wouldn't dare take a chance on Leo thinking that he had affected her choice of entertainment for the evening.

When they walked in, the music was already blaring, lights were flashing to the beat but there were no bodies on the dance floor. Too early yet for most. That didn't matter to the girls though; if a good song came on they would dance anywhere, anytime. No matter if anyone joined them or not. As a matter of fact, both of them at one time or another had danced alone on a dance floor. Of course, it usually took a couple of margaritas to get that far.

As they walked to the bar to order a drink, Shari saw Leo out of the corner of her eye, he was watching them. "Probably had been waiting for them to arrive," she thought. "I hope he doesn't ask me to dance, I am not ready for this."

Lily noticed the look on Shari's face and said, "Relax, we're here to have fun. What's the face for?"

Shari replied meekly, "Oh nothing, I was just thinking."

"Thinking about what? You looked terrified. Leo is not going to hurt you, he's a nice guy. Anyway, it's just a dance. It's not like you have to marry him!" Lily handed her a shot glass with some green liquid in it. "Here, this will keep your mind out of it. Let's dance."

They headed for the dance floor and a couple of other girls followed them. Shari tried to forget that Leo was there and probably watching her. It made her uncomfortable, but yet she was somehow curious about him. She would watch for him and make sure he was not watching her. She moved around on the floor positioning herself so that she could see the crowd near the bar. He wasn't there. She slowly turned her eyes toward the door and there he was; he wasn't watching her. He was talking to a couple who looked like they had just arrived. "Awesome," she thought. Now I can dance.

The rest of the evening she did occasionally check to make sure he wasn't watching. She made eye contact with him once but quickly turned her head as if she was looking for someone in the crowd. If he was watching her he was doing it carefully. She was OK with that, as long as she didn't catch him doing it she would be alright.

As they were coming off the dance floor toward the end of the evening, he met her at the edge of the dance floor and arm in arm spun her around like a square dance move. "May I have this dance?" Before she could say anything he had her out on the floor and the music was starting. It was a slow song. She dreaded this, she hadn't been this close to a man in months.

He was taller than she thought, and held her firmly but not too close. She was very comfortable with him, she felt no pending threat of an expected kiss or whatever it was that some of the other men there would expect. He was a great dancer; together they whirled around the room as if on air.

She was not experienced with this dance step and stumbled or stepped on his foot several times, but he was so graceful that he never missed a beat. She would apologize, but he would just smile and nod and keep dancing.

It felt as if the dance went on forever. She wasn't even sure she heard the last note of the song. She was far away and felt safer and happier than she had felt in over a year.

When he took her hand to lead her off the floor she cooperated, but it set her head to spinning. "What do I do now?" she thought. "Is everyone going to think we are a couple?" They approached her small gathering of friends, and he thanked her for the dance, kissed the back of her hand and walked back to his companion who was holding a pool game for his dancing friend.

Her friends immediately wanted to know what happened, how she felt, what would she do now; there were too many questions, and no answers. All she would do was smile and say, "It's nothing, we didn't even talk. It was just a dance." But Lily knew better, she could see it in her rosy cheeks. Shari was alive; all she had to do was remember what it was like and she would come out of her shell.

Lily, in the years they had known each other, had never seen Shari this way. She hated "him" for doing this to her once outgoing, boisterous friend. Her relationship with "him" had changed her and she hoped it was not forever. She wondered what he had done to her to make her this way. She had heard, and experienced some of his torture, but she bet that there was much more to it than she even knew. Hopefully, her friend would come back to her eventually.

They announced "LAST CALL" and the last song of the night started to play. Lily grabbed Shari and together they ran for the dance floor. It seemed too early to be heading home, but Lily knew that Shari would not want to go anywhere but home as soon as the music stopped. Lily would stay out till daylight if Shari would come along, but she knew she wouldn't.

Shari glanced around the room curiously to see if he was there. Their eyes met and locked for a second; then she blushed and turned away. "That's all," she thought. "He will just have to wait for me to be ready if he wants to get to know me. I'm not ready yet. I have to make sure that I don't think of 'Him' when we are together. That would ruin everything."

3 Getting On With Life

Shari awoke Sunday morning with a new outlook. She was not stuck in her old rut any longer. She felt good despite too much alcohol the night before and was happy.

The sun was out, and she could hear the birds singing. She hopped out of bed and found that Lily was still sleeping. "She may sleep till noon if no one bothers her," she thought.

She slowly and quietly put on her favorite yoga pants and a shirt and headed out for a stroll. There was a light breeze and the grass was damp with dew. A few leaves had started to fall but the rest would be a while, it was usually mid-October or November before they had colored leaves and the smell of autumn.

She picked up the pace and was doing a pretty brisk walk when she heard a car behind her. Her first reaction was to run and hide, what if it was "him," but she quickly put that thought away. "I have to get on with my life," she thought. "It's now or never. I won't be a prisoner to 'him' any longer. Anyway he doesn't know where I live and he lives an hour from here. He'd have to be a bloodhound to find me." With that thought she tossed it away and wouldn't think of him for several days. She was on the road to recovery.

When she returned from her walk, she was hot and thirsty. In the kitchen was her friend, looking rather tattered. "What's wrong?" Shari said.

"I think I ate a dead animal last night," teased Lily. She noticed that Shari had those rosy cheeks again. "What's up with you? You look, well...happy."

Shari said, "I just made up my mind, I have to get on with my life. Today is the first day of the new me. You want breakfast? That walk made me hungry."

Lily groaned, "No, yuck, food is bad. I'm going back to bed."

Shari decided to shower first, then made herself a cheese omelet. It was about ten o'clock, she figured she would give Lily till about noon, and then she would see if she wanted to go to the river. It was going to be another nice day.

About the time she was going to wake Lily, the phone rang. Shari didn't even reach for it. Lily had one by her bed, and it was always for her anyway. Then she heard: "It's for yooooouuuuuuuuu!"

"For me? Who would be calling me? My mom always calls my cell. Heck everyone calls my cell, I never give out this number." She picked up the phone and said, "Hello?"

"Hi, pretty lady. It's Leo. I just wanted to call and thank you for a great evening." Shari almost swallowed her tongue. She hadn't expected this. She swallowed hard, so hard he could probably hear her on the other end.

"Oh, hi, Leo. Thank you too, it was a nice evening."

He sighed and said, "Maybe we could do it again sometime?"

She was so shocked that she could hardly speak, she stammered and managed to choke out, "Umm, OK." Her mind was racing. She was rarely nervous like this around men. Was it him, or was it just her last relationship that

21

made her this way? She couldn't tell. She thought to herself, "You have to get a grip on yourself or he is going to think you're crazy."

He rattled on about something someone did or said last night, but she was not really listening. He mentioned wishing he had grabbed her earlier to dance.

She muttered something like, "That's OK."

He responded, "Well, you were having so much fun with your friends I didn't want to interrupt. Next time I won't make the same mistake."

She laughed sheepishly, not knowing what to say. She acted like Lily said something to her and said, "Oh, I'm sorry, Leo, but Lily needs my help with something, I have to go. Thanks for calling. I'll talk to you soon."

She could hear in his voice that he was smiling when he said, "OK, I'll hold you to that. See ya' later. Goodbye."

Lily was dying to know what was said. As soon as the phone was out of Shari's hand, she pounced on the couch. "Well?"

Shari just smiled and said, "It was Leo, he wanted to thank us for a good time."

"Us, hah! He wasn't thanking me for anything, you little fibber. I told you he likes you. I think you should give him a chance."

"I might," said Shari with a smile. "I just might. Hey, you wanna go to the river? I will fill you in on all the gory details there."

After Shari spilled all the details of her conversation with Leo, Lily asked her what really happened with HIM to scar her so badly. She couldn't imagine what could have made such a drastic change in her normally fun-loving friend, and since she was finally able to say she was moving on with life, she thought she might be able to tell her about it now.

Shari was reluctant to start, there were so many things

that happened; it wasn't just one incident that had affected her and changed her so much. There was a whole list of things, but she agreed it was better to get it out than to hold it all in. She had just not been ready to come face-to-face with it all yet. She started with no real order or plan but the details just started to come.

"Well," she said, "it's a can of worms, you could say. There are so many things, so many details it may not make sense when I explain it. I'm not sure it makes sense to me. I think I even blocked out some stuff because sometimes a certain smell or sound will bring some memory rushing back that I had forgotten about. He was a very odd person. Basically he had no self-esteem. He borrowed his self-esteem from other people around him."

Shari lowered her voice to almost a whisper. "Remember the time he went with us to that concert and he seemed to be having a great time? He was making little jabs at all the people around us, smart remarks that everyone actually laughed at but if you thought about it, the comment was absolutely rude or just mean. That's how he got through every day.

If no one was around to pick at, to make himself feel better he would either drink or take one of many prescription drugs that he had been given by some of his so-called friends. He slowly chipped away at my self-esteem by making backward compliments, like if he went somewhere without me, he would tell me when he got home, 'I looked all over the restaurant tonight and I could not find another person there as beautiful as you.'"

She took a deep breath and looked off into the distance and said, "I didn't notice it at first, and my self-esteem was great when we got together so him draining it little by little was not that noticeable to me. I didn't even realize I had started to gain weight until I saw a picture of us at a family gathering and I almost didn't recognize myself. I had packed on almost thirty pounds in a year."

Shari admitted to her intently listening friend, "All we ate was junk, and never did anything but watch TV. After he convinced me to move to his town and rent that expensive apartment, he changed. He decided to change jobs, which lasted about two months; then he was laid off and started to draw unemployment. All he did was lie on the couch all day. He would be up all night, and when I got home from work he would be sleeping on the couch. If I even got myself a drink of water, I got the look of death. I was a prisoner in my own home.

When we first got together he would call me as soon as I left work and we would talk on the phone till I got home; then we would either go out to eat or to the store or for a drive. After a while he stopped calling me, so I would call him. That lasted until he lost his job, then I would get yelled at for waking him up. I couldn't go somewhere after work because if I wasn't home at the right time, he would accuse me of doing something I wasn't supposed to and he would be angry, but if I went home all I could do was sit on the bed and watch TV because he was on the couch asleep. I couldn't do laundry, eat or even get a drink out of the fridge because he would be mad if I woke him up.

"Then he decided to stop smoking. I supported him and put up with his moods and tried to help him. We stopped going anywhere at all because he couldn't stand the smell of cigarettes. Then oddly enough, he started going out alone. He had done it a few times before, but he usually called me and asked me to meet him later.

At first I was not happy when he wasn't home when I got there, but he started coming in later and later and a couple of times he didn't come home at all! Once he came home in the middle of the night and dragged me out of bed by my feet. I landed on the floor on my butt in a pile of blankets. Thank God. I can't imagine how bad it would have hurt to land on the floor without them."

She felt like the words were just flying out of her mouth. "I couldn't say anything or he would scream at me to mind my own business. I started to hope he wouldn't come home, ever. I would hear his feet coming down the sidewalk and I would pretend to be asleep. It was horrific. I remember he introduced me to this girl who was at least ten years younger than him, stating that he was going to help her with her career. She wanted to work in an office and he was going to get her a job.

I of course thought it was crazy. There were jobs everywhere, but all he wanted to do was hang out with her and some of her friends all the time. It was really strange, and they all acted like they really liked me; one time one of them even asked me why I was with him. She thought he was an asshole. She spent more time with him than I did so I asked her the same question, and she said, 'It's business. He spends a lot of money in this bar so we keep him happy.'

"I never asked her what she meant by that, but looking back on it I think there was probably some funny business going on in that bar. I started noticing that he would have private phone conversations and leave in the middle of the night. I wasn't sure if he was selling drugs or running a prostitution ring, but I wouldn't put either one past him. I think that he even tried to pimp me out one time, but I wasn't stupid enough to fall for it.

The next day he tried to make me believe I was overreacting to his behavior. He made me doubt my own memory and made me feel like I was going crazy. I actually stopped drinking around him because I found that his lies were mostly backed up by comments like, 'You don't remember, you were drinking.' I decided that I needed to remember everything and be confident in my memory, so that I knew exactly what was happening to me."

Lily, aghast at what she had just heard, stated, "Wow, I never imagined it was that bad."

"That's not the worst of it," said Shari, "but I don't want to talk about it anymore. Let's talk about something else."

"Of course," agreed Lily, "you can tell me more later. Hopefully he has found some other unsuspecting person to torture and will leave you alone," and she really meant it. She wanted to know it all, no matter how ugly it seemed. She thought it might help Shari get it out of her head. More than anything she wanted her friend to heal and move on with her life. Shari was such a warm and caring person. It was hard to see her being so distant and untrusting. She started up a conversation about their fun summer to settle the mood. "Hey, what about that summer we had huh? I can't believe it's over."

What they didn't know was that he was still looking for Shari. He was absolutely not done with her and he had plans to make her pay for what he imagined she had done to him.

4 DREAMS

It was days after her conversation with Lily about him, but on her way home from work Shari heard a song on the radio that instantly reminded her of HIM and quickly changed the channel. "Damn HIM," she said aloud. "I was doing so well. I won't let it get to me." She wished the bad thought away and turned up the radio.

It was Wednesday, hump day. Halfway through the workweek. Lily always worked late on Wednesday, so Shari had a small bite to eat and went to bed early. She fell asleep watching old reruns of *I Love Lucy*. She loved how simple life was then. She rarely had dreams, or if she did she never remembered them. Tonight would be different.

She dreamed that she was babysitting for her sisters' children on a warm fall day. Her sister had three wonderful children and Shari loved them all very much. In the dream her sister had a large three-story house with a large garage. It was dark when her sister and husband arrived home, and they asked her to stay for dinner. She decided to stay, and when they went to put the children to bed on the third floor of their beautiful house she left to go home.

The garage door had been left open and she was parked inside with the top up but the windows down. It had cooled off quite a bit so she was rushing to the car and didn't see the shadow lurking beside the house. She had her coat bundled up around her neck, hopped into the car and started it up immediately rolling up the electric windows. Something distracted her. Did she see something? She looked in the rearview mirror and didn't see anything. Then suddenly there he was, it was HIM.

He had his hands on the window as if he was trying to keep it from going up. She let go of the window control and locked the doors instinctively. His hands were in the window almost to the palms so she tried the up button again. He yelled out in pain as he pulled back some, but then started pulling again on the glass. She was screaming at him, "Stop, stop, you're going to break the glass," not realizing that was his full intention.

She started hitting at his fingers, but he just grabbed back at her. He somehow managed to get a small handful of her blonde locks and she screamed in agony. Her sister and husband could not hear her from the third floor. She honked the horn frantically and reached for something, anything she could use as a weapon.

Through clenched teeth, he quietly, almost in a demon-like voice, said, "I'm going to kill you, bitch. You ruined my life. Bitch...Bitch...go ahead and yell for help, no one will come. No one will save you, bitch." She managed to pull her head away far enough from his painful grasp and reached the ice scraper on the floor below her feet. She started jabbing it at his hands frantically and slammed the car into reverse.

As he stepped back shocked that she actually fought back, she floored it and flew backward out of the garage onto the street. The garage was dark. She couldn't see him because her headlights were pointing past the house when she came to a stop. She rolled up the window the rest of the way and as she threw it into drive he came running in front of her car. She laid on the horn and punched the gas. He dodged the front fender and she sped away. She could see him standing in the street waving his arms in her mirror.

Suddenly she was awake. She was in a cold sweat, shaking and a bit confused. What had just happened? Was it a dream or was it real? Her heart was pounding. She could actually hear it. She took a deep breath and realized it was a dream. "Just a dream," she said to herself. She lay there for almost an hour before she drifted off to sleep, quietly praying for no more dreams.

Shari awoke to the alarm. "That's odd," she thought, "I never sleep until the alarm goes off." She jumped out of bed and tossed her hair into a messy bun, washed her face and quickly dressed for work. "This will have to do," she said to her reflection.

He hated it when she wore her hair that way. In his world she had to be dressed, made up and hot as he would remind her. "Hot girls don't wear ponytails or wear their hair in a pile on top of their head." She could hear him saying this repeatedly in her mind. She was never allowed to relax or take a day off from looking hot.

As she climbed into the car to leave for work she heard her phone buzz, but she quickly forgot about it as she was driving to work. It would not be until nine fifteen when she received a text from Lily that she remembered. When she picked up her phone to see who it was she almost dropped it again. She sat the phone down on her desk and placed her face in her palms. What could he possibly want from her? Why was he texting her?

She was afraid to even open the message. She decided to wait until lunch because she could already feel the anxiety and she knew she didn't need to look stressed in the office.

Her boss had already warned her about allowing him to distract her from her career. She was not sure what that meant but she did not want to find out.

At lunch she left the building and drove to a small park down the street. There was no need to get something to eat because she knew she would not be able to keep it down. She pulled to the far side of the park and stopped under a big tree. She swallowed hard and felt her stomach turn while she opened the message on her phone. She was relieved to see that it just said, "Hey, I need to talk to you. Please call me." Then her mind started spinning. What could he want? Why was he contacting her? Should she reply? She quickly called Lily for some support and advice. Lily answered on the second ring.

"Hey, what's up?" Shari swallowed hard and told her of the text. Lily had a usual response and it always made Shari feel more confident. "Fuck him! Delete that message and don't you dare call him. Why haven't you blocked his number?" Shari admitted that she was more afraid to block him than to see what he had to say. She felt like if he was blocked and started going off the rails she would not know. This way she could at least gauge his mood. She decided that Lily was right. She deleted the text, thanked Lily for her strong confidence and went for a short walk before heading back to work.

She tried not to think about it for the rest of the day, but as she went to bed she wondered what he might want. Those thoughts created another night of fitful dreams. She had the same dream as the night before. This time it felt even more real and it stopped at the exact same place.

5 Summer is over

Shari awoke to a cold, blustery, and cloudy morning. As she climbed into the shower and let the hot steaming water rush over her, she prayed for a good day. Sometimes just standing there in the shower with the water bouncing off of her skin was all she needed to feel human again.

As she prepared for her day she felt hungover from the night before, even though the only thing she did was have a nightmare. "Man, that one's a doozy," she said out loud to her reflection. It had felt so real she still wondered if it had actually happened in the back of her mind. "How could a dream feel so real?" she wondered. "Why would I dream the same one twice?"

She decided not to let the night before spoil her day and on the way to work she popped on her favorite music. She spent the brief drive listening to the radio, singing along and waving to the people she saw basically every day.

She worked on a couple of different projects and was in the middle of a phone call when someone rapped on her office door. She waved them in, not really looking to see who it was. When she put the phone down and directed her attention to the person standing in front of her desk she realized it was not someone from her office. It was Chuck from the local flower shop proudly sporting a dozen beautiful bright red roses.

Shari blushed and said, "Are you lost, Chuck?" assuming he was certainly looking for directions to an associate's cubicle or office.

He smiled from ear to ear with his slightly stained teeth that had a small gap in the front center and said, "Now, Shari, you know I know my way around this office! These are for you." She didn't ask who they were from, she was embarrassed to have Chuck know more than he already did.

As she reached for the roses, Chuck melodically chanted, "Theyyyyy're from Leeeee-oooooo."

Shari felt her cheeks get hot again and said mockingly, "Thank you for the singing telegram?"

Chuck snickered and hollered over his shoulder on his way out the door, "He's a nice guy, Shari."

Shari reached for the card, almost afraid of what it might say. She opened it carefully and as she was about to read the card the phone rang. She jumped and looked at the caller ID; it was Lily. She grabbed the receiver and glanced at the card as she said hello to her best friend. Lily said cheerfully, "Whatcha doin'?"

Shari teasingly said with a smile, "Guess what just got delivered to my office?"

Lily quipped back, "What? What is it? Is it good?"

"A dozen of the biggest, reddest roses I have ever seen," chirped Shari. "They're from Leo."

Lily was in a state of utter excitement at this point and insisted, "Is there a card? What does it say? Are you going to call him? I can't believe he sent you flowers!"

Shari interjected, "Whoa, Nelly, calm down. It's just flowers. Not a proposal!"

Lily asked again impatiently, "What does the card say?"

Laughing at her friend's incessant need to find out the

details she said slowly, "None of your business!" then giggled because she knew it was killing Lily to wait for the information. "It just says, 'Thinking of you.'"

Lily of course, took that and ran with it. "I told you he liked you. You should date him, he seems so nice. My friend Troy said he is a real stand-up guy. Hey, you there? Shari?"

"Oh, sorry," Shari said. "I was thinking about something else."

"What were you thinking about? This is important!" mocked Lily.

"Nothing," said Shari, "I better get back to work. I will talk to you later, kay?"

She fibbed to Lily, she was thinking of something. She was wondering if this flower business was a way of distracting her from his personality. "Is there something he is trying to hide, or is he just a nice guy?" "Damn it for not being able to trust anything anymore," she thought out loud. "Maybe I should go out with him, it would be a nice change." A small smile started to curl up the edges of her mouth as she remembered dancing with him. "Maybe I should," she thought. "Maybe I will."

The rest of her day went by so fast…it was already five o'clock when her boss passed by her office door and said, "You workin' late?"

Shari looked up and said, "Oh, hey…not intentionally. I guess I was just focused on this report. How was your day?"

Her boss smiled and said, "Typical for a Monday. I'll see you tomorrow." He paused at the door and said, "Or, would you like someone to walk out with? I can wait a minute."

Shari was gathering her things and smiled and said, "You know what? I'll take you up on that." Her thoughts were quickly of that dream, and a companion across the parking lot was a welcome distraction.

In the car on her short drive home Shari was glad she decided to leave the roses at work so she could enjoy them during the day and didn't risk damaging the gorgeous blooms on the road. She smiled remembering how sweet they made the whole room smell. No one had ever sent her flowers before unless they were apologizing for something.

She wasn't really sure how to take the gesture but she knew that wasn't the reason they were sent. She silently wondered if Leo was being nice or if he was trying to trick her into believing he was nice. She looked at her gaze in the rearview mirror and said to herself, "Only time will tell." Then she turned up the radio and sang the rest of the way home.

When she pulled up in the drive she noticed that Lily had not made it home yet and she shuddered at the thought of being home alone. That dream she had last night was still fresh in her mind and had suddenly popped back into her thoughts when she noticed she would be home alone. The neighborhood was safe. All of her neighbors were nice people and always helped each other out but she could not shake the feeling that she was being watched. She gathered her things and thought to herself, "I sure am glad I left the roses at the office. If HE saw them it would be a huge fight."

She quickly looked around and hopped out of the car, locking it on the way out and ran to the front door. She didn't even breathe until she was safely inside with the door locked behind her. "I hope Lily gets home soon," she thought as she peeked out the window to be sure no one was behind her.

"It's going to be a long night," she said to herself as she headed for the bedroom to find something more comfortable to wear. She hoped her most comfortable pajamas and a hot meal might just change her perspective.

Lily came rolling in like a summer breeze about an hour later with bags from the grocery store. Of course she was shocked to find the door locked and Shari snuggled up on the couch with a remote in one hand and a cup of hot chocolate in the other. Shari immediately said, "I'm sorry I locked the door. Something about this day just made me feel less safe than usual."

Lily was unfazed as usual and said, "It's OK, no reason to be nervous in your own home." Little did she know Shari was nervous everywhere since she had that dream. She just could not shake that feeling that HE was hiding in the shadows somewhere waiting to charge at her. It was a feeling that would take weeks to fade.

Lily quickly unpacked the groceries and said from the kitchen, "I'm making dinner. You didn't eat yet, did you?"

Shari was glad to hear that and said, "No, ma'am, and I'm starving!" Lily always seemed to know what to say to help Shari feel more at ease. She didn't think about the dream again until it was time for bed. She silently prayed that she would not dream that night.

The next morning she woke tired but was happy not to recall any dreams at all. Probably because she didn't sleep well enough to dream. "I'll take it," she thought to herself as she tried to freshen up her face for work. She didn't want to look distressed because it would bring too many questions from her coworkers who had watched her decline over a year ago into someone they didn't know. She wanted to avoid rumors and questions from her peers. They meant well but sometimes got too close. The last thing Shari wanted was to have to relive that nightmare every time she had a poor night's sleep.

Shari arrived at work a few minutes early and decided to

stop by the coffee shop for some extra energy and in her foggy mind didn't realize she walked right past Leo's truck on the way in. She stepped up to the line and was fumbling with her phone when he walked up to her and said, "Grande mocha, right?" as he handed her a steaming hot cup. Shari was startled and dropped her phone on the floor. As she bent to pick it up he apologized and pretended not to notice how tired she looked. He stretched and said, "Mornings like this make it hard to get motivated. It's so dreary today. Got a big day planned at work?"

Shari smiled as she sipped her piping hot cup of coffee and nodded. She then remembered the roses on her desk and said, "Oh, but I have twelve beautiful roses to brighten up my office. Thank you! They are so beautiful and they smell so amazing. I apologize that I didn't call you yesterday to thank you. Work was a little hectic and I…well, I'm sorry I didn't call."

Leo smiled one of the biggest smiles she had ever seen and he said, "I didn't do it for a thank-you. I did it to brighten your day and I am glad to see that it worked. No need to apologize." He held the door open for her to step outside and said, "I'm working in the neighborhood today, would you like to meet me for lunch? I could use the company."

Shari thought for a moment and could not muster up an excuse to say no so she said, "Yes, I'd like that."

Leo smiled as he turned to walk to his truck and said, "Awesome, you pick the place and text me. I'll meet you there. Unless you want me to pick you up?"

Shari stopped suddenly and said, "No. That's OK, let me think about it and I'll text you. I'll see you at about noon."

"He'll pick me up?" she thought. "That's all I need. I am sure the office is already buzzing about those roses. It's better to meet him somewhere off the grid. I wonder where we should eat? I'll have to think hard on that one."

Shari spent the next hour contemplating where to eat lunch—somewhere her coworkers might not see them together. She finally decided to meet him at a small sandwich shop that she loved a few blocks away. She would have to drive there and she doubted her coworkers would venture that far since there was plenty to eat near the office.

She was finally able to focus and worked hard to make up for her lack of attention for the beginning of the morning. She could not help but check the time over and over again. She didn't want to admit it but she was looking forward to meeting Leo. She wasn't sure why.

Part of her was afraid it was because he was another of those "bad guys" and the only reason she was interested was because of her bad taste in men. She silently prayed her curse was over in the man department. "I've suffered enough," she whispered to herself and grabbed her purse and walked out of her office to meet Leo.

Shari arrived in the parking lot of the sandwich shop Leo was standing near his truck and immediately walked to open the door to Shari's car. He helped her out of the car and walked her to the door of the restaurant and ushered her in like a gentleman.

He quickly located a table and pulled out a chair for Shari. He then said, "I've never been here before. Do they wait on you or do you order at the counter?" Shari informed him that it was faster to go to the counter but you could do it either way. "If you know what you want, you can sit here and I'll place the order," Leo said with a smile.

Of course, Shari knew exactly what she wanted. As he walked away Shari could not help but notice how gentle and kind Leo seemed. She wondered if he treated everyone with the same kindness as she was seeing. Opening doors, pulling out chairs. She would be paying close attention to his behavior, because she had learned from experience that words mean nothing. If you want to get to know someone you should watch how they treat others.

Leo placed the order and came back with drinks and a number for the table. "What a neat place," Leo stated. "How did you find it?"

Shari smiled gently and said, "Sometimes I like to get away from the office for a little while and this place is easy to get to. I stumbled upon it once when I was window shopping. I don't come often but it's a nice break from the typical workday and their sandwiches are amazing!"

When the waitress brought the plates Shari noted how Leo spoke to her. He was kind but not flirtatious. He smiled and seemed genuinely nice. The meal was pleasant and their conversation was easy. He didn't ask her any serious or intrusive questions. He didn't make any wild promises or have an opinion on every word she said. It was just a pleasant lunch. She would be careful not to create any ideals of how Leo was or how he would be in the future.

For now, she would be satisfied with the present moment. "What a fresh idea," she thought to herself as a small smile lifted the edges of her mouth. Her hour lunch was over way too soon. She glanced at her watch and said, "Oh, I need to run. I don't want to be late getting back."

Leo instantly jumped up and pulled out her chair for her. He said kindly, "Don't worry I'll get this cleaned up. I really enjoyed having lunch with you. I'll call you later if that's OK?"

Shari smiled and nodded shyly, feeling her cheeks get hot. She gave Leo a quick hug and said, "Thank you for such a nice lunch. We'll chat later. I have to run." She turned and slipped out the door into the sun with a big smile on her face.

She arrived back at the office and didn't even remember the drive. She was lost in happy thoughts and appreciating the sun on her skin. She could not remember the last time she felt so calm and free. She spent the rest of the afternoon happily working on projects in her office and didn't spend one minute dreading the future or worrying about the past.

At five o'clock her boss walked past her door and said, "Hey, it's quitting time," with a smile.

Shari looked up from her work and smiled and said, "Thanks, I didn't even realize what time it was. Have a great evening." As she walked to her car she remembered that Leo said he would call her later.

For a brief minute she wondered what time he would call but she quickly decided that it did not matter. She decided to stick to her normal daily routine and not watch the phone for his call. That's how she used to live and it had not served her well in the past so she made a commitment to herself not to allow her mind or a possible phone call to control her evening.

On the way home she stopped at her favorite roadside stand and grabbed some fresh veggies and strawberries for an amazing salad. She zipped home and tossed the fresh food into the refrigerator and changed so that she could get in a quick walk before Lily got home from work.

She was coming back around the block and breathing fairly heavily when her cell rang and she saw that it was Leo calling. She took a couple of long deep breaths so that she didn't sound like she was running from a grizzly bear and said, "Well, hello there."

Leo sounded distracted and she could hear noises in the background. He said he was caught up in some challenges at work and was going to be there a while. He just called to let her know that he might not be home until much later than he thought. "I just wanted to check to see that you made it home OK and remind you that next weekend there was a benefit dance at the town hall. If you and Lily are planning on going, I would like to see you there."

Shari responded with a "Thank you, and I'll ask Lily tonight."

He said, "You don't have to answer now, I just wanted to remind you. I have to go. Talk to you soon. Bye."

Shari said, "Bye," and was shocked that the conversation was so to the point and clear. "Interesting," she thought. "I must be overthinking things. I really need to stick to my rule of no expectations. He's definitely not acting anything like I am used to."

She stepped up onto the doorstep and felt a sigh of relief to hear Lily talking on the phone. She immediately went to the kitchen and motioned to Lily with the bag of fresh veggies and salad ingredients. Lily nodded excitedly. Shari went to work creating the best salad she had tasted in a long time.

Lily and Shari spent the evening chit chatting about her visit with Leo and watching some random shows on TV. Shari mentioned the benefit dance that Leo had asked about and Lily was excited. "I wanted to go to that. We should go." Shari smiled and nodded. She wasn't so sure but it was a week away so she let it go. Shari fell asleep easily with no thoughts of tomorrow or yesterday and no expectations.

6 SURPRISE

Shari was halfway through the workday when she heard a familiar voice in the office. It was just about lunchtime and as she looked at the clock she heard the voice again. She took a deep breath and got up to close her office door but was too slow. There he was looking her right in the eyes. "What are you doing here?" she said through clenched teeth. "You know you are not supposed to be here."

He gently pushed her back into the office and closed the door behind him. Shari moved quickly to the other side of her desk to create some distance between them, never taking her eyes off him. He said in his most charming voice, "Honey, I've been trying to reach you, but you aren't returning my messages. Honestly, I was concerned about you and decided I should check to ensure you are OK. Why aren't you returning my texts?"

Shari gasped and said sternly, "You need to leave. I have nothing to say to you."

He started to walk around the desk nearer to her and she moved to keep the desk between them. He then said, "Shari, honey. You know that I would never hurt you. Why are you avoiding me?"

Shari reached for her office phone and hit 0 and put it

on speaker as she moved further away from him. He quickly reached for the phone to hang it up but the office operator answered and Shari got one word out, "Help," before he disconnected the call.

He knew instantly that security would be on the way to her office and he had seconds to make his point. He started for her again but she was nearer to the door than him so she grabbed the knob and turned it quickly. As she opened the door he whispered to her through his tightly clenched teeth, "This isn't over, Shari. We need to talk." He then pushed her aside and strutted out the door as if nothing had happened and made a quick escape down the hallway.

Security came around the corner in time to see her knees buckle and grabbed her before she fell. Hot tears streamed down her face as they helped her into a chair. Jerry, the security man she had known for years, didn't have to ask. He knew instantly what had just happened. "Shari, are you OK?" he said quietly. She shook her head yes as her friend Susan handed her a tissue. Jerry winked at Susan and took off down the hallway. He was determined to find out how he got into the building without permission. As he walked away he said confidently, "This won't happen again, Shari."

Shari wiped away her tears and stood up. Embarrassed by the attention she had attracted, she apologized and went back into her office but Susan was right behind her. She sat quietly in the chair opposite her desk for quite some time before she could see that Shari had regained her composure. Then Susan said, "Shari, I am so sorry that he got in here. This is not supposed to happen. We have security measures to prevent it. I am going to personally find out what happened and make sure that he doesn't get in here ever again. I also think you should file a restraining order against him."

Shari nodded and quietly said, "Thank you." She knew a

restraining order would not stop him from getting to her. It would only make matters worse. She silently wondered if she should move away. Her mind was racing. "What if he is in the parking lot when I leave? What if he follows me home?" Her brief time of feeling safe and distanced from him was over.

Jerry came back and said that he had left the premises and he found that someone had propped the door open to go to their car for a minute and he must have sneaked in during that brief period. Which means he had been waiting for the right opportunity. Jerry asked her if she wanted to go home early and Shari shook her head no. "OK, but I am walking you to your car every night from here out."

Shari agreed it was for the best. "Thank you, I would appreciate that," she said sheepishly.

Jerry replied, "This isn't your fault, Shari. You don't need to feel responsible for his behavior. I am happy to make sure you are safe and don't worry, we are making a company wide announcement about that door being propped open. Someone was careless."

It was near quitting time when Jerry and Shari's boss both popped their heads in her door. Shari looked up from her computer and said, "Hey! I get two security guards tonight, I guess?"

They both nodded and held the door open for her to walk out. As they were walking to the door her boss said, "Shari, have you considered getting a different car? Maybe it would be a good idea. Something he might not recognize you in. I am concerned about your safety. I don't want him seeing you drive by and follow you. As a matter of fact, here are the keys to my car. Let's trade cars for a few days. It would make me feel so much better."

Shari blushed and said, "No, sir. I can't ask you to do that for me. I will be fine."

Her boss smiled big and opened the door to his car and said, "I won't take no for an answer. I'll take your keys. Be safe on the way home and I'll see you tomorrow."

Shari smiled and said, "Thank you," as she closed the door of her boss's luxury sedan.

Shari drove home feeling overwhelmed with the kindness she had experienced. She had no idea that her office family cared so deeply for her safety. It was a good feeling. When she arrived home Lily was in the driveway unloading some groceries and said, "Where did you get that car?"

Shari replied, "It's my boss's car. He basically forced me to take it home because asshole showed up at work today and he didn't want him to be able to follow me home."

Lily stopped in her tracks and said, "What? He—wait! I thought you had a secure building?"

Shari shrugged her shoulders and said, "A determined person always finds a way. My boss thinks I should get a different car. What do you think?"

Lily raised her eyebrows and said, "You love that car. Why can't that asshole just leave you alone! I can't believe after all these months he just shows up at your job. He must be really desperate. What did he want?"

Shari sighed and said, "He wants to talk, apparently." Then they both laughed out loud and went into the house, carefully locking the door behind them.

Shari filled Lily in on the details of the brief visit from her ex. Oddly enough, she wasn't nearly as emotional about it as she thought she would be. She was concerned though about him just showing up like that, and wondered how long he had been watching her office building to see how to get in like he did.

Shari had accidentally left her phone on silent and didn't notice that it had been going off since she got home. When she went to bed she saw that she had twenty-five texts and four missed calls. She grabbed her phone and went straight to Lily's room. She handed her the phone with a solemn look on her face and said, "Will you look at these? I just can't."

Lily grabbed the phone eagerly and said, "Oh yeah." As she read the messages she raised one eyebrow and looked up at Shari and burst into laughter.

Shari breathed a sigh of relief and said, "What is it?"

Lily smiled and said, "He's apologizing. He actually says here that he met someone else and wanted to clear the air with you but he got angry when you were trying to avoid him. He thinks you are going to ruin his new thing."

Shari was shocked at this news yet also very relieved. "Do you think this means he will leave me alone? What should I say? Should I respond?"

Lily said, "I think you should just say congratulations and I wish you the best. Here, I'll text it for you. Maybe if he is really with someone and his belief is that you are happy for him he will move on and leave you alone." Lily quickly typed a brief message into the phone and hit send. "There. It's done. I guess we will see if he's telling the truth."

Immediately a response came back. It was two words, "Thank you."

Shari smiled and thought, I sure hope this is true. "Thank you, Lily. I sure hope this is the end of it." Shari went to bed with a smile on her face. She didn't fully believe it was over, but she was certainly hopeful and a little hope was all she needed to sleep.

She was excited to tell her boss the next day that he should not be back, but her boss was not so quick to believe it. He wanted Shari to keep his car for a few more days to be sure he wasn't following her. "Safety first," she thought. "We shall see." She said a silent prayer that it would be true.

A couple of days had gone by and Shari was back to driving her own car again. She missed it so much but since it was colder out she rarely had the opportunity to put the top down. It was Wednesday, Lily's late workday and as Shari got ready to leave work she thought to herself, "It sure feels warm today. Maybe a little top-down time would be good for me."

Feeling the wind in her hair and the radio up was always a great way to improve her mood. She wound up her hair into a bun and grabbed her favorite sunglasses out of the console and slid them over her eyes. Excited to feel the wind in her hair, she turned onto the street and cranked up the radio. She was free, happy and in her favorite place. As she made the turn into her neighborhood her phone rang. It was Leo. She smiled and answered, "Hello, sorry it's windy. I decided to ride with the top down one last time before winter hits."

Leo laughed and said, "Good for you. I know you love a good top-down day. Hey, what are you doing tonight?"

Shari thought for a second and said, "Nothing that I know of; Lily works late on Wednesdays so I usually just hang at home."

Leo replied, "I am grilling some steaks at the house. Would you like to come over for dinner? My friend Joe and his girlfriend, Celine, are also coming."

Shari took a deep breath in and thought, "Why not?" "You know what, Leo? That sounds great. Can I bring anything?"

"Just yourself," Leo said with an obvious smile on his lips. "See you around seven."

Shari arrived home a little before six and was suddenly nervous. "Oh my. What should I wear? Will we be outside

or inside? It's already almost completely dark so, layers ...
Yes, layers, comfortable layers." She found a great pair of
comfortable jeans that fit just right and a cute top in the
closet. Then she went to Lily's closet and grabbed her best
flannel overshirt to top off the outfit. She put on her new
boots with the fur on the inside just in case and took a
minute to refresh her hair and makeup. "Why am I so
nervous?" she whispered to her reflection. "It's just
dinner," she said to herself and she walked out the door.

She arrived at Leo's house a few minutes early and
knocked on the door. She heard him holler from the
interior of the house somewhere, "Come on in." She
opened the door and was surprised at how beautifully
decorated his home was. It was clean, not cluttered and
very well designed. The open floor plan made it very easy
to find him in the kitchen near the patio door.

He was holding the patio door open with one elbow and
had his arms full of steaks and grill tools. She ran to the
door to hold it open and he slid out. "Welcome to my
home," he said with a bow. He placed the steaks and
barbecue tools on the table near the grill and said, "Can I
get you something to drink?" Shari nodded with a smile
and followed him into the kitchen where he opened the
refrigerator and pointed out several options for her. He
said, "I was just going to open a bottle of wine if you would
like to choose one."

She leaned forward to see what the options were and
settled on a nice bottle of red. "Here, this one looks good,"
she said as she handed it to him. He opened the bottle and
poured them both a nice glass and led her back out to the
patio.

She found a comfortable seat near the grill and sat down
with her glass. Leo went about the job of getting the steaks
on the grill and organizing his tools. She was intent on

watching him work. He had such purpose and seemed so comfortable and confident. His friends arrived and made their way to the patio as Leo lit the outside heater to add a little warmth to the seating area.

Joe and Celine were an awesome couple. They were kind and invited Shari into their conversation as if she had always been a part of their group. They watched Leo make an amazing meal while they chatted and laughed at the occasional joke inserted by Leo. The evening was brisk but beautiful. Sitting outside near the heater made it perfectly comfortable and the wine didn't hurt either. The four of them had a fun evening and the meal was delicious. She had never met the other couple but admired how they spoke to each other. They seemed to be a really good match. About ten o'clock Shari looked at her watch and said, "Oh, I should go. Work in the morning."

Leo got up from his seat and walked her to her car. "Thank you for coming. I hope you had a good time," Leo said.

Shari smiled as he opened her car door and replied, "It was a perfect evening. Thank you so much for inviting me."

Leo leaned in and kissed her on the cheek and said, "I hope we can do it again sometime soon." He closed her door for her and stepped back as she drove away.

She looked in the rearview mirror and he was still standing there in the middle of the street waving. She could not help but smile as she drove away and she could not wait to tell Lily about her evening. "What a gentleman," she thought as she pulled into the driveway.

Lily was waiting for her as she came in the door with a glass of wine and lots of questions. The two girls stayed up for another hour laughing and talking about the evening and all of the possibilities that could come from it. Shari was excited but also nervous about the implications of this evening. "He was the perfect gentleman but doesn't he want something in return? When is he going to start to make demands of my time or my body?" She went to bed a little confused but mostly just happy that she had such a nice evening.

7 PANIC ATTACK

It was Thursday. Shari was used to not having plans for a Saturday night but this week she was agitated. Leo had not mentioned anything about the weekend but she felt like he was expecting to see her. It was just something he said. "Does he think that because he called me Wednesday at five and I showed up at seven that he doesn't have to make plans in advance? Did I make a mistake going over there?

Well at least I didn't kiss him or overstay my welcome. I don't even know why I thought he would call." Her mind was working overtime and all of her fears were amplifying her lack of confidence. "Well, I will show him," she thought. "I won't answer the next time he calls. This is too stressful. I don't even know why I went over there. I am such a fool." Shari had forgotten about the benefit dance that Leo had asked about the week before.

Shari arrived at work earlier than normal but she had a key to the office so she went on in. The janitorial staff and some other employees were bound to be there too. She stepped into the stairwell to go to her office and for some reason the light was off. She grabbed her phone to help her find a light switch. She flipped it up and down and nothing, the bulb was burned out. She suddenly felt anxious. As her throat began to feel tight her hands started shaking and as she turned to go back out the door she dropped her phone. She pushed on the door but it didn't open.

In her panicked state she didn't realize that she had to turn the knob to open the door and she pushed again. When the door didn't budge she lost her composure.

Now it was black, she could not see her phone and she was trapped. Her heart started pounding and she could hear it in her ears. Her face was getting hot and she felt weak in the knees. "OK," she thought. "This is a panic attack. You've been here before. Think. Think, Shari! What are you going to do?"

She was literally holding her hands over her own mouth to silence the audible scream that was bubbling up from somewhere deep in her soul. She was sobbing out loud now. She put her back against the door and slid down to the floor. Her eyes were burning from hot tears, and her throat was tightening more and more. As her eyes slowly began to adjust to the darkness she could see a low glow from the door at the top of the stairs. "Stop it!" she yelled silently to herself. Her mind racing and heart pounding was keeping her from thinking clearly. It was so dark. She reached out and searched for her phone. It had to be right there somewhere.

As she started to find her bearings she heard her mom's voice in her mind. "Shari, can you smell that?" Shari stopped reaching for her phone and took in a big breath through her nose. "What can I smell?" she thought. "I smell leaves. I smell fall. I smell a trash can with cigarettes, yuk." Her breath started to slow and she thought, "What else?" Her mom had always told her when you feel like you are going to panic, use your senses. Smell, hear, taste, touch, see. "Well I can't see much. I do see a little light and I can see my hand now. My eyes are adjusting to the dark. What can I hear? I hear a fan. Maybe the heat for the building? I hear footsteps. Oh no! Footsteps. What if it's him? Did he cause this? Is he waiting for me to run back out of this door? OMG!"

Her calm went straight back to panic mode. She was now crawling around the floor looking for her phone. "There it is. I found it." She flipped it over and touched the screen and the light came on. She then turned on the flashlight and made her way quickly up the stairs. She burst through the upstairs door and ran to her office, turned on the light and locked the door behind her. She sat down on the floor behind her door and cried. "Why am I such a mess?" she thought. "Normal people don't act this way."

She took a minute or two to calm down, got off the floor and sat at her desk. She left the door locked and would wait until she knew it was safe to open again.

Susan was the first one to notice she was in the office with her door closed. She gently knocked and was shocked when Shari got up to unlock the door. Susan stepped inside and closed the door behind her. As she sat down across from Shari at her desk, she said, "What happened?"

Shari looked at her with wide eyes and took a deep breath. Then she said, "Nothing. Nothing happened. I came in the back stairwell and the light bulb was burned out. I tried to go back out but because of the safety features I didn't realize I had to turn the knob. I panicked. I had a full-blown panic attack in the stairwell. I feel so stupid. I am a total wreck. I should probably go home. This is so embarrassing."

Susan got up and walked around the desk and bent down to look Shari right in the eyes and said, "Shari, you aren't stupid. You have been through a traumatic experience. You have every right to be afraid. Have you talked to anyone about your situation?"

Shari nodded and sniffled. "Once. I went to a therapist but I felt so stupid. I felt like I had no right to ask for her help. It's not like I was battered or put in the hospital. I was just afraid of what he was capable of. That he might, you know? That he could possibly hurt me. I don't have any evidence. He told me that no one would even believe me. He said I was being oversensitive and that I was making it all up." Shari was sobbing again.

Susan wrapped her arms around her friend and just sat there with her for what seemed like a very long time. When Shari stopped crying Susan leaned back and said, "I have a friend who works with victims of abuse. I am going to give you her number. Please call her. You can't continue to do this yourself. You need someone to talk to who understands your perspective."

Shari nodded and wiped her face. She took the number and jammed it down in her pocket. "I'll call her later," she said. "I'm too upset right now."

Susan smiled and walked out the door. As she closed it she said, "Maybe you should take the day off. Go get a massage or something."

Shari knew she was right. There was no way she was going to be able to focus at all. She opened the contacts on her phone and looked up the number of her favorite massage therapist and sent a text. Fortunately she replied immediately. "Hey, girl! I had a cancellation. Can you be here at ten?"

Shari gladly accepted the appointment and called her boss to let him know she was taking a personal day. "Oh and the light bulb in the back stairwell is out. See you tomorrow," she said and grabbed her purse to head to the car.

She arrived at the spa a few minutes early and sat in the car in the sun for a while. The sun felt so good on her face.

She thought about her morning and how she quickly came so unhinged in that stairwell. "If the door had only opened I would have been fine," she thought. "It wasn't my fault." She remembered the number in her pocket and took it out and put it in the console of the car. It was time for that massage. Shari was whisked into her friend's massage room with a clean robe and some fresh coconut water.

Tawnie had been her massage therapist for years and was so glad to see Shari. "Where have you been, girl?" she said quietly.

Shari shrugged and said, "Oh, just busy."

Tawnie said, "Well, make yourself comfortable, busy girl. I will be back in five."

Shari got undressed and sipped on her coconut water. The sounds and smells of the spa were so relaxing. She climbed onto the table and closed her eyes. She could feel the stress already melting away. Tawnie came back into the room and adjusted the lights and the music. She added some soothing lavender oil to the air and said, "Where's your trouble area today?"

Shari opened her eyes and said, "I am just a mess. I had a panic attack this morning. I need some de-stressing."

Tawnie raised her eyebrows and looked intently at Shari. "A panic attack? Really? What happened?"

Shari told her about the dark stairwell and why she thought she lost her cool. "I just feel like if the door would have opened I would have been OK."

Tawnie added some warm oil to her hands and started on Shari's shoulders and said, "Well, I can feel the tension in your neck. Are you sure that's all it was? I mean are you usually afraid of the dark?"

Shari thought about that question for a minute. "No, I am not afraid of the dark, or at least I didn't use to be. I am just easily spooked these days. You know, since the breakup."

Tawnie made a clicking noise with her tongue. "Oh, I see. It makes sense now. Has he been bothering you?"

Shari shrugged her shoulders and said, "Well he did show up at the office a couple days ago and he claims he just wanted to tell me he was dating someone else but it scared me to death. He said he was just trying to fill me in so that I would not ruin his new relationship."

Tawnie stopped massaging for a second and said, "Don't you find that weird? He hasn't spoken to you in months and suddenly he is worried you are going to contact him? I find that odd. Has he contacted you since?" Shari shook her head no and thought about the implications of Tawnie's comment.

"It was odd. I guess it doesn't really make any sense that he did that, does it? Well he's not bothered me since so I hope it's true."

Tawnie shrugged and said, "I do too, Shari. Please be careful though. That's odd behavior if you ask me."

Shari agreed and said, "I promise, I will. Let's work on getting rid of this stress. Which does not include thinking about him."

"Agreed," said Tawnie.

Tawnie gave Shari the works at the spa. When she left to go home she felt like a new woman. She gladly took a bottle of fresh cucumber water made by her own Tawnie for the road. "This stuff is amazing. Thanks for the awesome massage. I'll see you again soon." Shari was driving home and decided she would spend the rest of the day resting. It felt so good to be relaxed. She arrived home and went straight to the bedroom, put on pajamas and dragged a blanket to the couch. She popped on the TV and looked for some old comedy movie to keep her company. It didn't take long for her to fall asleep on the couch, which is exactly where she was when Lily got home from work.

When Lily opened the door Shari was shocked. She immediately jumped up and ran to the bedroom. Lily was stunned and followed her. "Hey, are you OK?"

Shari stopped and turned to look at Lily. Her face was still all scrunched up and Lily could tell she was not OK. Shari immediately burst into tears and said, "No, I'm not OK. This is the second time today I have panicked. I went home from work early because I freaked out in the stairwell because it was dark and I thought I was trapped. Now I am flipped out because you came in the front door. What's wrong with me? Why am I such a basket case?"

Lily looked at her dear friend with love in her eyes and said, "Honey, you have been through a horrible experience and that asshole showing up at your work the way he did probably set off a whole new set of issues for you. I don't blame you for being jumpy."

"It's not OK with me!" cried Shari. "It's not OK!"

Shari went directly to the car and got the phone number out of the console. She sat on the couch with the blanket around her shoulders and texted the number. "Hi. You don't know me but I am a friend of Susan's. She said I should contact you about getting help."

Within a minute the phone beeped. "Hi, Susan's friend. My name is Mel. Susan told me someone might be calling me. Are you OK? Are you safe?"

"Yes. I am safe. My name is Shari and I need someone to help me make sense of some feelings I have been having. I am having panic attacks all of a sudden for no reason and I don't like this feeling. Can you help?"

Mel replied, "Of course I can. I have an office near where Susan works. Can you meet me for lunch tomorrow?"

Shari smiled and responded with, "Yes. I work with

Susan and I would love to meet you tomorrow."

Lily was relieved to see that Shari had finally agreed to talk to an expert. She tried to help her but she didn't know how to truly help. She sat down on the couch next to her and said, "Shari, I can see you are really struggling right now. What can I do to help you feel safe?"

Shari smiled and wiped a tear from her eye. She took a deep breath and said, "Lily, you are one of the best friends a girl could ever ask for. You just being here makes me feel safer. I am so glad you had room for me in your house and that you keep me so busy all the time. I think staying busy all the time has helped but I think it's time for me to face my fears. Ignoring them is not going to make them go away. I need someone to help me figure out how to put all of this behind me so that I can be happy again."

Lily wrapped her arms around Shari and hugged her tightly. "Shari, you know I love you. I want you to be happy again too. I am here to support you in any way that I can. I will even go with you to your appointment if you need me to. I want you to get your life back."

8 MEL

Shari was up before the alarm and jumped in the shower immediately. She was looking forward to talking to Mel at lunch. She drove to work with an energy that she had not felt in a while. Was this excitement? Excitement for a new future? "Gosh I hope so," she said out loud to the face in the rearview mirror.

Shari's morning went fast. She had received a text from Mel asking her to meet at the park. Shari gladly walked down the block to the park in the sunshine. She could smell the fall leaves, and the sound of the wind blowing the leaves down the street always made her love fall. It was such a welcome feeling. The day was warm but the wind was cool. She walked around the bend at the park to see a woman sitting on a park bench with a brown poodle on a leash. The dog was beautiful and jumped up and wagged his whole body to greet Shari. "Hello, puppy!" Shari said with a smile. "I'm Shari. Are you Mel?"

Mel smiled and reached out a hand to Shari. "Yes, what a beautiful day to be at the park. I am so glad to meet you. I hope it's OK to meet here."

Shari nodded as she reached down to pet the beautiful brown curly locks on the dog's head. "How do we do this?"

asked Shari.

Mel smiled and motioned toward the park bench. "Let's get to know each other."

Mel asked Shari a few questions like where she was from, how long she had worked here and about her support system. Shari was proud to say she had Lily and Susan as well as some of the people in her office like her boss and Jerry looking out for her as well. Mel was glad to hear that Shari had some really supportive people in her life. Mel then asked, "Are you dating anyone?"

Shari frowned and looked at Mel. "Not really. I have someone I have seen a few times but it's not serious. He's just a nice guy. I am not even sure if he's really interested in me. I mean he seems interested but honestly, I am not sure I am interested in dating. It's all so confusing. I feel like I'm damaged goods. These panic attacks I am having would really be a bummer on a date! I just don't know if a guy would even want to mess with me. I am such a wreck."

Mel smiled and said, "You are not the first one to say that to me. Often, women feel like they are damaged goods and that no one will be able to tolerate their moods or attitude or behavior after a breakup like you experienced. Did your ex tell you that you were any of those things? Like hard to get along with or crazy?"

Shari looked at Mel like she was a genius. "How did you know? He used to tell me that I was crazy or overreacting all the time! If I said anything at all about how he was acting he always made it out to be my fault." Mel nodded in agreement. Shari continued, "It was impossible to argue with him. He would start an argument with me, then make me feel like I was the one who was being unreasonable and like I started the argument. It was infuriating."

Mel nodded again. "I understand completely. That is also something I hear a lot of. I sponsor a support group for abused women on Wednesday evenings. I know it's not something that you are used to doing but would you come and just listen?"

Shari leaned back on the bench and took a deep breath. "Mel, I wasn't abused like most women. I wasn't beaten. I never had a broken bone. I really don't feel like I belong in a room with women who have real stories to tell. I guess I could come listen but I don't feel like I would have any input of value."

Mel smiled a warm and knowing smile, then nodded in agreement with Shari. "Shari, I know that you feel like you don't have a story to tell, but I think this group might be helpful for you. I really would like for you to come."

Shari thought about it for a minute. She shifted in her seat and leaned forward and put her face in her hands. Mel waited patiently for Shari to process her thoughts. Shari looked up at Mel and said, "OK. I'll come."

Mel winked at her and said, "If you want you can bring your friend Lily with you." She stood up and tossed a ball for the dog to chase.

Shari stood and smiled as he ran for the ball. "Thank you, Mel. I'll see you Wednesday. Enjoy the park. I better get back to the office." Shari walked casually back to work, enjoying the sun and the smells of fall. She was almost back to the office when her phone rang. She looked at the screen and saw it was Leo. She paused for a second and thought, "Should I tell him I need some time? If he really knew what I was going through would he want to see me? What if he finds out I'm crazy and doesn't want to see me anymore?" She silenced her phone and slid it back into her pocket. "Not today Leo. Not today."

As she rounded the corner of the building her phone beeped to let her know she received a voicemail. She smiled and swiped her badge to go into the back stairwell to her office but paused to make sure the light was repaired before she closed the door. As she did, someone grabbed the door and swung it open further and she thought for a second it was him. She immediately thought, "Oh no! I should have paid more attention." Her heart started racing and she could feel the anxiety starting. As she turned around abruptly she was relieved to see Jerry's smiling face.

He said, "Hello, sunshine! How was your lunch?"

Shari took a deep breath and forced a smile. "It was really good," she replied, even though she didn't eat at all. She was too excited to hear what Mel had to say. Lunch could wait. As she entered her office she took a moment to focus on her breathing and slowing her heart rate. It took a few minutes to reach a state of calm but she did it. She smiled a big smile and patted herself on the back for her achievement.

The rest of the day was quiet. She wrote on her calendar Mel on Wednesday so she would not forget, but she knew she wouldn't. She was excited even though apprehensive for the meeting.

As she walked to her car she listened to Leo's message. "Hey, Shari. I'm sorry but I have been really busy at work. I intended to talk to you about Saturday. I'll be home this evening if you want to call. Talk to you later."

9 WORRY

Shari hopped into her car and dialed Leo's number. It went straight to his voicemail and she sighed with relief. She hung up and sent a quick text. "Thanks for your call. I apologize but I have plans for Saturday." She really didn't have plans but she felt like she was doing Leo a disservice by leading him on. Who was she kidding anyway? She wasn't ready to date anyone. Shari headed home to spend the night on the couch. Of course, Lily would argue but she didn't care.

Shari arrived home to see Lily already showered and ready to go. "Hey, what's your plan?" Shari said as she tossed her purse on the counter.

"Oh I just thought you might want to go grab a bite to eat somewhere."

Shari shrugged. "It's been a long day."

Lily came back with, "OK. Perfect, then you don't feel like cooking. Let's go."

Shari could not argue her logic so she picked up her purse and said, "Where to, ma'am?"

In the car on the way to the restaurant Lily said, "Hey don't forget tomorrow is that benefit dance we were planning to go to."

Shari had forgotten. "Shit! I bet that's why Leo called today. Now I feel like an ass."

Lily looked shocked and said, "Why? What did you do?"

"Well, I sort of told him I had plans tomorrow," Shari said meekly.

Lily laughed and said, "Well, we do." They pulled into the parking lot and right out front was Leo's work truck. Shari sat there for a second and thought about her message. Lily winked at her and said, "Come on. It's just Leo. No biggie."

They walked into the restaurant and were taken straight to a booth in the corner adjacent to the bar. From where they were sitting they could see Leo sitting at the bar with a man and a woman they did not know. Lily leaned over to Shari and said, "I wonder who she is?"

Shari turned her head back quickly and said, "Who cares!" but she did care. She was a little shocked to feel a pang of jealousy and then immediately went into a feeling of distrust, thinking privately to herself that he was probably dating this woman.

The waitress took their orders and as she went to the bar to grab their drinks Leo turned and made eye contact with Shari. She smiled and turned back to Lily. Lily made a face and said, "What's that about? Did you two have a fight?"

Shari laughed and said, "No. What would we have to fight about?"

"Well, You look a little mad," teased Lily.

Shari stuck her tongue out at Lily and was glad to have the waitress show up with drinks. As they were waiting for their food they saw Leo get up and pay his bill. He then turned and walked straight for their table. Shari shifted uncomfortably in her seat as he stopped at the end of the table and said, "Hi. How are you both enjoying your

Friday?"

Shari smiled and nodded shyly and Lily said, "It's good so far. Who's your friend?" Shari kicked her under the table and Lily moved to avoid another kick while giving Shari the evil eye.

Leo turned and looked back to the bar where he had been sitting and said, "That's Missy. She's new in town. She's working for the vet. Seems like a nice lady. Hey, are you still planning to go to the benefit tomorrow?"

Lily smiled a big smile and said, "Wouldn't miss it. Right, Shari?"

Shari nodded and smiled at Leo, remembering her text from earlier in the day. "Yeah. I guess we will see you there."

Leo smiled and said, "Perfect. Can't wait. See you tomorrow." He turned and walked out the door.

Lily smiled at Shari and said, "See. No worries." But Shari was worried. She was very worried.

10 THE DANCE

Saturday was a beautiful day. The sun was out and it was warmer than usual for this time of year. Lily and Shari spent some time digging through their closets looking for the perfect dress to wear to the benefit. It would be cowboy boots and dresses for this afternoon and evening. The weather would be perfect for a light jacket and if there was to be dancing a dress provided the proper amount of ventilation.

When they arrived at the benefit everyone had the exact same idea. There were cowboy hats and boots everywhere. It looked like a great turnout and they were excited to see so many people show up to raise money for a good cause.

Shari and Lily found a table near the front so they could be close to the dance floor and live band. As they were getting comfortable at their table they saw Leo and his friend Joe and his girlfriend come in the door. Lily waved and they came straight to the table. "Have a seat," she said. "We have plenty of room."

Shari was still nervous but made an effort to have a good time. When the band started she was feeling pretty good and had probably had a little too much of that punch they were serving. She looked at Leo and said, "What is in this punch? I think it's spiked."

Leo looked at her and could instantly see why she asked. Her cheeks were rosy red and she was looking pretty relaxed. He chuckled and said, "Shari, that's moonshine. How many have you had?"

Shari's eyes got really big and she leaned over to him and thought she was whispering, but she wasn't. "Only three. I'm fine. It's fine. Totally fine." Then she winked at him and slapped his leg.

Leo looked at Lily who returned his shocked look and burst out laughing. Leo reached over and grabbed Shari's hand and said, "Let's get you moving," as he led her to the dance floor. Shari was so loose that she was ready to dance to every song.

She kept Leo on the dance floor for four songs in a row and then Lily came to relieve him. She swooped in and said, "Hey, Shari, have some water," then winked at Leo. "I have not seen her this drunk in forever," she said over the loud music.

Leo laughed and said, "I'll be back." He sauntered off to a group in the corner while Lily kept Shari on the dance floor.

Shari threw her arm around Lily and said, "That Leo is something isn't he?"

Lily nodded and spun Shari around on the dance floor. "We need to get you sobered up."

Sobering up was not in the cards though for Shari. She was having a blast and was completely relaxed. She ran to the back of the hall and grabbed Leo's arm and swung him around. He happily obliged and she said, "Come on, let's dance." Off to the dance floor they went. When the song was over a slow song came on and this time instead of trying to avoid the slow dance she happily leaned into Leo as he wrapped his arm around her.

They danced and talked and swayed to the music. Leo was a fantastic dancer and he spun her around the dance floor like a princess. Shari didn't notice but her friends were watching and thought they looked like they had danced together for years. When the dance was over the crowd applauded. Shari blushed and looked at Leo and said, "Are they applauding us?"

He winked at her and said, "I think so. You make me look good."

The night was over way too soon for Shari. She had just enough of that moonshine to make her forget all of her troubles for the night. She had fun. Real fun. Leo walked her and Lily to the car and fortunately Lily was aware that the punch was spiked and had chosen not to drink any.

Before Leo poured Shari into the passenger seat she turned and gave him a big hug and kissed him full on the lips. Lily almost swallowed her gum. Leo chuckled and closed the car door and Lily winked at him. He walked away with the biggest smile on his face. Lily climbed into the car and said, "Put your seatbelt on, honey."

The next morning Shari woke with a headache and slowly got up to make some coffee. She was surprised to see Lily already awake and up. "What time is it?" Shari said.

"Eleven," Lily said with a laugh. "You had quite a good time last night."

Shari smirked at Lily and then her eyes got really big and she said, "Wait. Did I kiss Leo?"

Lily laughed out loud and said, "Yes, you did. I think he liked it, too."

Shari put her hand on her head and said, "Oh no."

Lily replied, "Oh don't worry about it. He knew you had too much to drink. I'm sure it's no big deal."

"No big deal? How is it no big deal?" Shari said impatiently.

Lily smiled and said, "It's too late now to change it so let's not get stuck on it. I'm sure it's fine."

Shari could not forget that she kissed Leo though. It was all she thought about the rest of the day. How could she face him again? What would he think? It was too much to consider. She didn't want to start anything with him and then she went and kissed him. What a dumb move.

Shari woke up Monday morning to a text message from Leo. "Good morning, Shari. I hope you had a relaxing day yesterday. I'll be working in your area today and I would love to grab coffee with you this morning."

Shari waited until she was ready to leave for work to reply. She wasn't sure how to face him but she figured she might as well get it over and done with. She replied, "OK. I'll meet you at the coffee shop." She wasn't sure how to approach the topic with him but she was going to tell him she wasn't interested in a relationship. She was also going to apologize for her behavior and give him a chance to run before he got too attached.

Leo was outside the coffee shop when she walked up. He opened the door for her and ushered her in. He walked her to a table for two and said, "I'll be right back with your coffee."

Shari said, "Make it a big one, please." He came back with two large cups of hot coffee and sat at the table with her. She blushed and said meekly, "I feel like I should apologize for my behavior the other evening. I had no idea that punch had moonshine in it. I am so embarrassed."

Leo smiled and leaned in to whisper in her ear. "I thought it was cute. You have nothing to be embarrassed about." Shari blushed again and wiggled in her chair. She was obviously uncomfortable and Leo wasn't sure how to make her feel better. He asked her, "Is this about the kiss?"

She lowered her face and said, "Yes. I'm really sorry."

He reached over with one finger under her chin and raised her eyes to meet his and said, "Shari, I like you and you have no reason to apologize. As a matter of fact I would kiss you every day if you would let me."

Shari stared into his deep brown eyes and felt a sense of safety there. Her shoulders relaxed and she smiled at him and said, "Really? You don't hate me for being drunk?"

He laughed and said, "Shari, you weren't obnoxious. You were just having fun. It was cute. No harm, no foul."

She was so relieved to hear that he wasn't upset with her. He looked at his watch and said, "I better get you to work." He got up and walked her out the door. He said, "Do you want me to walk you to your office?"

Shari replied, "Actually, I would like that if you have the time." As they walked down the block she admired his stature and chiseled features. He really was a handsome man with wide shoulders and he was tall and confident. She liked walking with him.

He got her to the office and as he turned to go back toward his truck he leaned in and kissed her forehead. "Have a great day." Then he walked down the block back toward the coffee shop. Shari stood there for a minute and just watched him walk away. She admired him. She could not explain it but she felt safe around him. She had been feeling like she could not trust her own judgment but for some reason he was getting to her. She was slowly starting to believe he was different.

11 WEDNESDAY

Wednesday evening came so fast. Shari had it on her calendar but she had not told anyone other than Lily that she was going to the meeting. She had received the address by text from Mel and she was excited but also afraid to show up.

She walked to the meeting room and decided she would just sit in the back and not draw attention to herself. When she opened the door she was not expecting to see so many faces. There were women of all ages and colors in the room. Many were drinking coffee and some were just sitting quietly in the metal chairs, which were in a circle.

This wasn't what she expected at all. Mel immediately welcomed her into the room and offered her a beverage and a place to sit near her. When the meeting started Shari was really uncomfortable. She felt like she did not belong there—like she was an observer, and an unwelcome one at that.

The first person to talk was a domestic abuse survivor whose husband had broken her arm three times, her cheekbone once and her eye socket once. Her face was slightly misshapen where the last fight had broken her eye socket. She looked worn and tired. Her hands shook when she introduced herself to the group but her voice was strong and courageous. She had gone down the path of drugs at one point to hide her pain but she had been clean for a year. You could see how broken she had been in the past but also how strong she had become. Her eyes lit up when she talked about her kids and the new job she had just started that was going to improve their lifestyle dramatically. All of these women were cheering her on and giving her applause for her victory.

The next woman was young. She might have been eighteen. Shari did not want to ask but this woman had four children with someone who abused her mentally, financially and physically. Shari really felt out of place here. She was starting to feel like she should leave. She could not relate to these women. Their lives had been shattered by the physical abuse they endured. It was so hard to see them but so amazing to hear their stories of recovery and victory—how they escaped and got their lives back, how they stood strong and filed for divorce in the face of fear. Shari sat there in silence until the third woman started speaking.

Lisa was a tall woman. She was easily six feet tall. She was very thin and her voice was so quiet. When she began to speak, everyone in the room had to hold their breath to hear her voice. Her story was quite different from the others. Lisa had been a professional. She was a physical therapist and had her own office. She was smart and successful before she met her abuser.

Shari thought, how can a woman like her be abused by a man in this way? Someone like me? She listened carefully to Lisa's story. Lisa was successful; she had everything she thought she ever wanted. She met a man at a cocktail party and he was so charming. He whisked her off her feet and was so perfect. He became her best friend. He moved in with her and began helping her grow her business. He even worked in her office and claimed to have experience in her field and was helping her with patients.

Eventually he started managing her books and taking care of insurance accounts for her. He convinced her to fire her long-term office manager and let him handle the office. It wasn't until a woman came to her office to accuse him of stealing her money that she became aware of his behavior.

He of course claimed this woman was lying about the insurance fraud he committed but Lisa had become suspicious and started paying more attention. He was slowly breaking down her self-esteem and making her feel insecure about her practice. She struggled to maintain a steady client base and when she went to see her accountant about her taxes for the year, the accountant let her know that money was missing from her accounts.

Not only was he tearing down her self-esteem, he was stealing from her business. When she asked him about it he tried to convince her that she had made errors in the checkbook and that she was the reason it was not balancing. He completely convinced her that the accountant was wrong and made her hire someone else to do the accounting—someone he chose.

He completely bankrupted her and left her penniless. She had to sell her practice and her house to pay back the money he had stolen. She was now trying to rebuild her life and her business. Her heart and her spirit were completely broken. She was struggling to survive after being so successful. Shari was heartbroken to hear her story.

Mel stood up after they shared their stories and said, "You see? Not all abuse is physical. It's insidious and it sneaks in under our defenses and steals your confidence and self-esteem. The methods of abuse are many and multifaceted but the end result is the same. When you are afraid and you feel like you have nowhere to turn, you end up losing faith in yourself. You feel like you can't make your own decisions or trust your own intuition. Abusers want you to rely on them for everything while making you feel guilty, shamed or stupid for needing them, which creates a vicious cycle that's really hard to break."

As the group started to pack up for the evening Mel walked over to Shari and asked, "How do you feel about tonight?"

Shari shrugged and said, "I feel out of place. I don't feel like I deserve to be in the room with these amazing women. They are so brave and strong and their stories are so much more shocking than mine."

Mel nodded and said, "I understand how you feel. I am sure many of them felt the same way before coming here. Would you have time to stop by the office this week so we can have some deeper discussion?"

Shari nodded and a tear formed in the corner of her eye. She quickly mopped it up and said, "Which day works for you?"

Mel said, "How about Friday at lunch?"

Shari nodded and whispered, "See you then." Shari walked to her car, feeling sad and out of place. Those women in that room were so brave. How could she even tell her story in that room after hearing theirs? She felt like maybe he was right. She was overreacting. Full of doubt, she closed the car door and blasted the radio to drown out her thoughts. Friday was not too far off and she could not wait to hear what Mel had to say about her situation.

Lily was home when she arrived and asked, "How was the meeting?"

Shari shrugged and said, "I felt like a fraud and so out of place. You should have heard some of the stories those amazing women were telling. I don't have stories like that to tell."

Lily looked her right in the eye and said, "Your story is yours alone. No one can take it away from you and I promise not one of those women in that room would tell you that you don't belong there. I think you are being too hard on yourself. Did you make an appointment with the therapist to talk separately?"

"Yes, Friday," Shari said meekly. "I guess I will see what she says." Shari turned her head as a tear fell from her cheek. She took a deep breath and said, "It's my fault. He used to tell me that no one would believe me and that I was making something out of nothing. He said that I felt like a failure because I didn't apply myself and that I had a guilty conscience because I lied all the time. Maybe he was right."

Lily tried not to look shocked but sat down next to Shari on the couch and took her hands in her own and looked her right in the eyes and said, "Shari, I have known you for over five years. In that time I have never once thought of you that way. You are good, honest and kind. You have a successful career and you have so much potential. I have never heard you lie and you are certainly not a drama queen. He was wrong and he was manipulating your emotions. I am so glad you have an appointment with that therapist Friday. I hope she can help you see that what happened to you is real and not your fault."

They hugged a long hug—the kind that cures a broken heart. Shari felt so connected to her friend and was able to let out a deep sigh. "Thank you, Lily. You are truly THE best friend."

12 THERAPY

Thursday was a normal day. Boring actually. Nothing out of the ordinary happened and Shari thought to herself on the way home, "This I like. Boring is my new norm." Shari decided to take a longer drive home than usual to take in some of the fall foliage and just listen to the radio. She never even heard her phone beep when a text came through. When she got home she packed up her work things and went directly to the bedroom. "PJs and TV are on my calendar for the evening." She grabbed a snack and headed toward the couch with her phone in her pocket. She didn't even see the text she had received.

Lily was happy for a TV night, too. They both spent the next hour watching some old rerun and didn't speak at all. Shari's phone beeped and she pulled it out of her pocket to see a message from Leo, and one from a number she didn't recognize. She opened Leo's message first with a big smile on her face. It said, "I hope you had a great day. I would love to do that again."

She texted back a brief "Thank you. Yes me too," then decided to read the other message she received. Assuming it was spam she opened the message with the intention of deleting it when her face went completely white.

Lily saw her expression change and said, "What? Is everything OK?"

Shari shook her head in disbelief. "It's a message from his new girlfriend. She wants to ask me something."

Lily stood up and grabbed the phone out of Shari's hand. Staring at the screen, her face wrinkled with disdain, she said, "When will this ever stop? This is ridiculous!" She handed the phone back to Shari and sat down. Shaking her head she said, "Do what you want but I would delete that and not reply. He probably put her up to it."

Shari sat there in disbelief. Her good mood was gone and her mind was racing. "What could she possibly want from me?" she asked Lily. "What makes her think I want to talk to her?" She tossed the phone on the ottoman and decided she would think about it later and went back to the TV to drown out her thoughts.

When it was time for bed Shari could not shake that text. Why would she message me? What could she want? Is it just a way for him to be in my life? She picked up her phone and stared at the screen. Out of curiosity she replied, "Hi. I apologize but who is this?"

She stared at the screen as the tiny dots appeared at the bottom that showed she was receiving a reply. They went away, then came back and went away again. She was like, "What in the world is happening here and why is it taking so long for them to reply?" She wondered if it was him, using someone else's phone. Then it popped up. It read, "I can't talk right now." Shari felt a sudden surge of panic for this person she had never met and thought, "I hope she's OK." She knew better than to reply again. She did not want to create any drama for herself or for this stranger. She put her phone on the nightstand and fluffed her pillow. She lay there for a long while before sleep came.

She had that dream again. Equally as disturbing but this

time there was another person in the shadows. She could not tell if it was a man or a woman but she felt like it was ominous and scary. She woke in a sweat and looked at the clock. Her alarm was ready to go off any second. She turned it off and sat up rubbing her eyes and shaking her head. "This dream is weird. Why do I keep having the same … well sort of the same dream?" She looked at her phone and there were no more messages from the stranger. She shrugged and thought, "Good."

Shari was eager to speak to Mel today. She grabbed a couple of protein bars from the cabinet and stuffed them into her purse, thinking, "No lunch for me today." She got ready and drove to work with a curious smile on her face. She was excited about meeting Mel and couldn't hide it.

Lunch came so quickly. She quickly made the short trip to Mel's office and was greeted by the nicest woman. She had such a warm and loving smile. She could see why Mel hired this woman to be her front desk manager and the first face her clients would see upon entering her office. She made it feel safe.

Mel opened her office door and said, "Shari, come in please. How are you feeling today?"

Shari smiled and said, "I feel pretty good but something odd happened last night. I am hoping you can shed some light on it for me." She sat in the comfortable chair across from Mel and saw the room had several boxes of tissues. The thought of crying had not crossed her mind. She hoped that she didn't cry. She was really good at holding back her tears, usually.

Mel started the conversation with a brief intake form, basic information and nothing stressful. She then said, "I can see you are eager to be here. I appreciate your openness and readiness to heal. Tell me about last night."

Shari reached into her pocket and pulled out her phone.

She was embarrassed that she responded to the stranger the previous evening and felt like it was a mistake in the light of day. She also wasn't sure why she felt so compelled to reply. She handed her phone to Mel and said, "I'm sorry. I probably shouldn't have replied to this person. I don't even know if it's a real person. It feels a little like a trap."

Mel nodded her head and said, "Don't beat yourself up. You have been conditioned to be available at all times. It's absolutely OK for you to never respond to that person again. Have you ever heard the terms *love bombing* or *devaluing?*"

Shari stared at her wide-eyed and said, "No. Should I be familiar with them?"

Mel smiled a comforting smile and said, "Not necessarily, but you will be soon." Mel adjusted herself in her seat and said calmly, "Tell me about the beginning of the relationship you left earlier this year. What was it like to meet him and be around him?"

Shari leaned back in her chair. She closed her eyes and thought back to the beginning of their relationship. She stammered a bit when she started speaking because she was so unsure of her words. "Well, I, um. Hmm. This is harder than I thought it would be."

Mel nodded and smiled, waiting patiently for Shari to speak again. "It was great. When I met him he was so loving and sweet. He would literally do anything I wanted. He did things for me all the time. He would take my car for the day and detail it or get the oil changed for me. He sent me flowers and brought me wine. He was such a good listener. He asked me questions about my dreams and plans for the future. It was easy to see that we were very compatible from the start.

I was excited to have all of his attention and he wanted all of the same things I wanted so it seemed to be perfect in every way. Like we were meant to be together."

She paused and took a deep breath, readjusted herself in her seat and looked at Mel for encouragement. Mel smiled and nodded so Shari started again. "We talked about everything—our past, present and future. He always made sure to include me in all of his future plans and said we would do all of those things together. I see now what he did. It seemed so perfect I never realized that he might just be agreeing with everything I said," Shari blurted out. "How did he do that? Why did I fall for it?"

Mel smiled and said, "He was reading you, getting to know you and he wanted you to feel safe and secure with him."

Shari shook her head and said, "Isn't that what you should expect from a partner?"

Mel took a deep breath and replied, "Yes, to some degree but if you look back at the happenings of this relationship you might recognize that it was too much, too soon. Also, you might notice he didn't tell you about his hopes and dreams at all did he?"

Shari adamantly nodded her head yes. "That's all we talked about—our future and how we would be so happy and doing all the things I wanted to do." Shari stopped and blinked hard. "Wait, you're right. He talked about my dreams like they were his. He never once disagreed with me unless it was to make my dream bigger. Oh my God. How was I so blind to this? I did this to myself!"

Mel raised her hand as if to say hold on and said, "You did not do this to yourself. You were blinded by the intensity of the relationship. It was everything you had ever wanted, right?"

"Yes, it was," Shari said. "I see now though that it was too perfect."

Mel smiled and said, "This is love bombing. He was

winning you over by lavishing you with love and gifts. It's overwhelming and so exciting that your body begins to release love hormones. This is how he enticed you to fall in love with him so quickly. He then used logic to lock it in, saying things like, 'I have been looking for you for so long, I can't believe I finally found my soulmate.' I bet he even compared you to his past relationships and made you feel like he had some really bad experiences with other women, too. Did he?"

Shari's eyes got really big and said, "How do you know that?"

Mel laughed and said, "It's a pattern. He wanted you to feel sorry for him and he was also training you. He wanted you to know what made his last relationship miserable so that you would not do those things. It may or may not have been true but the concept is to allow you to believe you are changing your behavior to protect him from further hurt and to make sure you don't mess up and lose him. You see, the devaluing and manipulation started from the minute you met him. It was just so subtle you didn't see it. He is an expert at this behavior."

Shari felt her eyes well up with tears. She thought silently, "No, you are not crying about this. You are not going to cry over him ever again." She reached for a tissue and blotted her eyes. She looked up at Mel again and said, "What else? Please tell me more about this."

Mel looked deeply into Shari's eyes and said, "I know you want to blame yourself for getting into this situation, but it's absolutely not your fault. He is a master at winning people over. It's what he does. If at some point you had called him out on this behavior he would have just left, discarded you. He would have recognized that you saw through his game and he would have disappeared, most likely with no explanation or he would have started a fight with you to see if you could be sucked back in. This fight would have left you confused, alone and afraid to lose him. If you apologized and tried to fix it, then he would have known you were his. Did you ever argue early on?"

Shari shook her head and said, "No. I hate confrontation so I would have never argued."

Mel nodded her head and smiled. "You can see then how he got you into this love bombing phase so easily."

Shari nodded and said, "Yes, I literally handed him the keys to the kingdom. I am such a fool."

Mel shook her head no. "You are not a fool. You are a kind-hearted, smart and lovely woman. You wanted to share your future with someone who seemed perfect in every way. That doesn't make you a fool." She glanced at her watch and said, "It's getting close to time for you to go back to work. Is there anything else I can help you understand better today?"

Shari wrung her hands slowly and said, "You mentioned another word earlier. Devaluing? What does that mean? I guess it means reducing the value of something but how does it apply to this situation?"

Mel looked her in the eyes and said, "Devaluation, in this context, is when someone uses your own shame and guilt, which we all have, to make you feel inferior or at fault for things in your relationship. He may have stopped texting you good morning or acted like he was angry with you, but would not say why. It's an attempt to gain control or the upper hand in the relationship. Usually it's subtle hints or behaviors that make you want to fix things. Ultimately, it's very confusing for you because you haven't done anything wrong but you feel like you did. Can you relate to that feeling?"

"Oh yes! I can relate to this feeling now," Shari said. "So him giving me the silent treatment or saying I overreacted to something no one else even noticed is an example of that?"

Mel nodded. "I know you need to get back to work but has this been helpful for you today?"

Shari nodded eagerly. "I am so fascinated by this. Can I schedule again for next week? I want to learn more about this."

Mel nodded and said, "Same time next week? Also can I expect to see you Wednesday for the group?" Shari nodded and stood up. She felt a smile start to work its way up the sides of her mouth. Her eyes were wet with tears but she felt good, like a giant weight had been lifted off her shoulders.

She stopped at the front desk to confirm her appointment and pay for her visit. She felt a sigh of relief as she stepped out onto the sidewalk. She walked back to her office pondering what she had learned. Love hormones? They must be powerful. She was familiar with stress hormones and wondered if they were the same. She was curious enough to start an Internet search later in the day.

She got a simple understanding of them and decided it was too deep a subject to look at during work so she closed the browser and decided she would learn more later. For now, she would be satisfied with learning how she got herself into this situation in the first place and sincerely wanted to learn how to never, ever do it again.

She also decided she would not reply to any more messages from strangers or feel guilty for not responding to anyone she didn't feel safe speaking to. What a relief that was. She thought out loud to herself, "I don't have to reply to anyone or anything I don't want to." She was completely unaware of it at the moment but she had just created her first solid boundary.

The Ties That Bind

13 ANYTHING GOES

Shari caught herself daydreaming. She was literally sitting at her desk staring out the window when she dropped the pen she was holding. It startled her briefly and she began to laugh at herself. It had been such a long time since she had any sort of daydreaming episode. She forgot it was even a thing. She was instantly hit with a twinge of guilt for not working and turned back to her computer. She had a few emails to reply to and a report to send but otherwise her day was pretty slow. The fall chill in the air and the smell of the leaves had her feeling dreamy. She loved this time of year because it was so fragrant—smoke from fireplaces, the leaves and cedar trees, cinnamon at every shop. They were the smells of fall and she loved them. It was also the best season to wear just about any outfit with boots—dresses, leggings, jeans, even shorts if the perfect situation availed itself. "It's anything goes season," she thought and laughed out loud to herself.

She finished her work and it was only four o'clock so she peeked into her boss's office and said, "Hey, I'm finished for the day and I don't want to start a new project this late on a Friday, so do you mind if I sneak out early?"

Her boss looked up and smiled with a big nod and said,

"Absolutely, you totally deserve it. Have a great weekend. Do you need me to call Jerry to walk you out?"

Shari shook her head no and said, "It's not quitting time. I'm sure I'll be fine."

Shari cleared her desk and grabbed the four jackets she had accidentally left on the hook from days when it was warmer and she had forgotten to take them home. Abandoned jacket season was her favorite season. She headed to the car and stopped briefly to take in a deep breath of the fall smells. Leaves were raining down from the trees in the mild breeze, the sun was shining and the temperature was so perfect for a fall day. She hopped in the car and headed off toward home.

As she rounded the roundabout in the center of town near the big clock she saw Leo's truck at the hardware store. He was putting some things in the back of the truck and waved big to her so she stopped. "Hello, beautiful! Aren't you off work early?"

Shari blushed and said, "Yes, I snuck out before dark!" She giggled as he laughed. Suddenly she got the urge to ask him what he was doing later. "I know it's short notice but what are you doing tonight?" she asked.

His laugh turned to a big grin and he said, "Are you asking me out?"

Shari blushed again and said, "Well, I, uh. Yes, I am. I thought it would be a great night to have some drinks around the firepit. I am craving hot apple cider and s'mores. Must be the weather."

Leo thought for a minute and said, "I think I can make that happen. Wanna come to my place? I think I have everything we need already." Shari smiled and nodded in agreement. Leo took off his ball cap and ran his fingers through his amazing blond wavy locks and said, "I'll be home by seven. Any time after that is fine. Come on over when you are ready. Invite Lily too, if you like."

Shari nodded and then remembered Lily was working. "Lily has to work this evening so it's just the two of us."

Leo smiled and nodded with a wink and said, "Even better. I'll see you later."

Shari took her time getting home and as she passed the shopping center she thought, "Hmm, I should grab something to bring with me to Leo's. Maybe a nice cheese plate or something." She swung the car around and made her way to the store. The smell of cinnamon and nutmeg was everywhere in the store. She could not help but smile as she looked for her cheese plate. She was far away and deep in thought when she was bumped rather hard by a shopping cart. She turned immediately to apologize to whomever it was for being in their way and saw it was him.

He had a young sheepish-looking blonde with him. She was tall and lean like a Pilates trainer, she thought to herself. Her makeup was perfect and her hair was in the most beautifully polished bun. Despite her beauty she had a childlike stance. It was so unsettling to see her with him but her appearance was more shocking. How could someone like her not exude confidence? He immediately started talking to Shari like they were best friends. "Hi, Shari. Imagine seeing you here," he smirked.

Shari was shocked to see them but also not sure if it was an accident or on purpose. He didn't live here. What was he doing in her town? She faked a smile and said, "Just doing some shopping. What are you doing in this neck of the woods?"

He pointed to the girl with his thumb like a hitchhiker and said, "Her mom has a house here. We came to visit for the weekend."

A wave of cold ran over Shari like a dark winter's night. Her hair stood up all over her body and she had to remind herself not to show any emotion. Shari squared off her shoulders and said, "Well, I hope you enjoy your stay. I have to run. Take care." With that she turned and abandoned her plan to buy cheese for the evening. She made a direct line to the exit and headed straight to her car. Once inside she locked the doors and took some deep breaths. He was in her town. How can she even go to the store now without looking over her shoulder? She shook it off and cranked up the radio. Heading for home she reminded herself that she was in control and no one could ruin her night.

She was ready earlier than anticipated because of getting off early and then cutting her shopping short so she was at Leo's right at seven. He was busy carrying some wood over to the firepit when she arrived. She had let herself in the front door and saw him through the back windows. She walked out the back door and said, "I feel like I'm early."

Leo shook his head and said, "Never."

He walked with her back into the house and they prepared s'mores and apple cider with a little bourbon for some fun. They sat around the fire with a blanket and talked about his work and the beautiful weather. Shari was a little hungry and she was kicking herself for not staying at the store and getting her cheese and sausage plate organized. She looked at Leo and said, "I wish I had brought the cheese plate I was thinking about bringing. I'm a little hungry. Those s'mores are not doing the trick."

Leo smiled and said, "I didn't expect you to bring anything. I do have some food in the fridge, or we can order a pizza if you like." Shari decided pizza sounded amazing. Leo grabbed his phone and quickly ordered from the local handmade pizza place. "Should be delivered in about forty-five minutes," he said.

Shari looked deep into his big brown eyes and said. "Can

I tell you something?" Leo didn't speak, he just looked back at her kindly and nodded. Shari took in a big deep breath and tried to calm her nerves. She had never really discussed her past with Leo but she felt he needed to know about him. If he was going to be in their town and possibly run into them somewhere she didn't want Leo to be surprised.

After all he was very unpredictable and the last thing she wanted was for Leo to be caught in the crossfire. "I ran into my ex at the store today. He doesn't live here and I never expected to see him. He is a bit unstable and I feel like you should be aware in case we run into him somewhere when we are together. I am afraid it might cause some sort of altercation. He had a woman with him but I didn't recognize her. He said her mom lived here and they were in town visiting but I have my doubts about his intentions." Leo nodded and smiled. He was waiting for her to finish talking before he said anything.

Shari continued. "I am sure you have heard through the rumor mill that I had a bad experience with him. It's not a secret. I am not very comfortable talking about it at all, but I think you deserve to know a little about it since you seem to be interested in spending time with me."

Leo leaned back in the chair and took a sip of his apple cider. She could tell he was thinking about what to say. She felt panic starting to build in her stomach and it was rising to her chest when he took her hand and said quietly and calmly, "Shari, I know you have a past. I am sorry that some asshole had to treat you so badly that you are afraid to go to the store in your hometown. It's not supposed to be that way. Women should be cherished and protected, not the other way around. I am not worried about men like him. I doubt he will have the backbone to say or do anything while I am around. Are you concerned about your safety? Do we need to go talk to the sheriff?"

Shari took in a long, deep breath and said, "God, no. That would only make things worse. He doesn't know where I live so I don't feel like that's necessary. Although he has shown up at my work without notice before. My boss even made me drive his car for a few days last month to avoid him following me home."

Leo raised his eyebrows and said, "He showed up at your office? Was he waiting by your car when you came out of work or what?"

Shari shook her head no and looked down. She was ashamed to feel so helpless. "No, he came into my office. Apparently someone had propped a door open to run to their car or something and he saw the opportunity and took it. He claims that he only wanted to tell me that he had a new girlfriend and wanted to let me know so that I didn't cause him any trouble with her but I can't see the logic behind that. I have never contacted him."

Leo laughed and said, "He's messing with you. Don't let him get under your skin. No one does that. No one." He ran his fingers through his hair again like earlier that day and Shari noticed that she felt safe with him. She admired his calm demeanor and that he didn't automatically ask if he should defend her honor or something. Her ex would have been ready to "make him pay" or something equally as disgusting. Leo looked deep into her eyes and said, "I think you need to take some self-defense classes. It would improve your confidence and it would help you feel safer. I have a friend who teaches women's self-defense and if you want I can go with you to the class."

Shari was shocked to hear those words. She had never considered the need to defend herself but she had been so afraid. Maybe that would be a good idea for her to do. She nodded and said, "Yes, I think that might be a good idea. I would love to feel more confident when I am alone."

Leo clapped his hands together and stood up. Smiling at her he reached for his phone and dialed a number. "Hey, buddy. When is your next women's self-defense class? Oh…that's a while off. Well, I have a friend who needs some classes sooner than later. What are you doing Sunday afternoon?…Great." Leo looked Shari's way and nodded to her as if he was asking her permission to make plans for her. She nodded in agreement.

"How about I barbecue Sunday afternoon and I can introduce you to her. Maybe you can even teach her some easy and quick moves to make her feel safer? Wonderful. I appreciate you. Bring your wife; see you then." Leo hung up the phone and smiled at Shari. "It's all set."

He sat back down just as the doorbell rang. "Time for pizza," he chuckled. "I'm starving." He rubbed his belly like it was fat and said, "Let's eat." The rest of the evening was so relaxed and fun. Shari laughed and enjoyed Leo's stories of the work he did and some of the characters he worked with. He never said a mean thing about a single person. It was like he truly loved and appreciated all of his coworkers. It was truly a refreshing way to be. Shari was floating on a cloud when it was time for her to go home.

Leo walked her to her car and suddenly got a serious look on his face. Shari froze. She quickly looked around to see if there was some sort of danger nearby. Leo opened her door for her and said, "I will follow you home to be sure you get there safely. Wait here. Let me get my keys."

Shari was stunned. Did he see something that made him concerned or was he just being cautious? He came back in just a moment's time and said, "OK. I'll follow you." Shari put her car in drive and started driving. Normally she would have declined the escort but her run-in at the store earlier that day had her a little nervous and honestly she appreciated having someone care for her safety.

She pulled up into her driveway and asked Leo if he wanted to come in and say hello to Lily who had just arrived home from work. He winked at her and said, "No I better get back home; I just wanted to be sure you were safe. I'll call you tomorrow." He drove away as Shari entered the front door.

Lily was unpacking some groceries in the kitchen when Shari walked in. "Hi, where have you been? Was that Leo's truck?"

Shari smiled and nodded. "Yes, it was. I went to his house for the evening and I told him that I literally ran into my ex at the store today. He hit me with his cart! He had a new girl with him but she didn't look OK. She looked like a rabbit that was ready to run in an instant."

Lily was looking at Shari intently with anger on her face. "Why in the world was he here? He hit you with his cart? Did it hurt? What the heck? I am shocked. What did Leo say?"

Shari smiled and explained the whole situation to Lily. She had a hard time hiding her excitement when she told her about Leo's friend who was going to teach her some self-defense moves to help her feel more safe. Lily smiled and said, "I knew you two would hit it off. He is such a nice guy. I am so glad you told him about the store situation. I think learning self-defense is a good idea for you."

Shari nodded quietly. Her thoughts were drifting. She suddenly remembered the look on the face of the woman who was with her ex. She could not help but feel a pang of guilt or concern for this woman and wondered to herself, "What was she feeling? Why did she look so off? Was it just the uncomfortable situation or was there more to it? Why am I so worried about her? UGH."

When it was time for bed, Shari drifted off to sleep but it wasn't a restful sleep. She could not get that eerie feeling out of her gut.

14 Sins of the father

Shari woke to the sound of leaves falling. She could hear them hitting the windows and the roof of the house. At first she thought it was raining but it was big yellow and red leaves. So many leaves. She remembered how as a child her friends would pile them up and jump into them. She remembered the smells and the laughter. She lay there with a smile on her face for a while, just reminiscing. She wondered if it was warm enough to go for a walk but then heard the gust of wind that was responsible for the leaves falling and realized walking would not be enjoyable.

She climbed out of bed and put on her robe. It was freshly washed and smelled like her grandmother's house. She loved spending time there as a child. She taught her how to do laundry the right way. This thought made her laugh out loud. "My grandmother ironed underwear." She chuckled out loud at this memory.

Her favorite memory of laundry day at Grandma's house was the sheets hanging on the line. She remembered walking between the rows of hanging sheets and could feel them sway in the breeze. She would run her fingers down the sheets on both sides of her and breathe in the fresh scent of clean summer air. It was her favorite memory of childhood. She often thought she could hide in the sheets. It was like her own world there—a freshly scented, summer breeze, private world to her. She relished in this memory for a while. Her grandma was one of her favorite people on the planet and she had been gone too long already. A happy tear slid down her cheek as she remembered how loved and safe she felt at Grandma's house. That was another time. "I'll never feel like that again," she whispered to herself.

Shari remembered her home life. It was normal, she thought. She had a mom and a dad who both loved her. They did divorce early in her childhood but that was for the best because they argued aggressively and it was terrifying to watch. She felt so helpless to help her mother when she cried after a fight with her father. She would be inconsolable for what seemed like hours after one of their fights and he typically stormed off and went to the bar.

Shari was so little and unaware at the time. She didn't know part of the reason her mother was so distraught over the fight was that he would be back and the fight wasn't over. The second act would be long after the children were asleep. Her father would return drunk and his anger would not be cooled from his time at the bar. It would be amplified.

She never knew her mother lived in fear every day of their marriage. The mom she knew after the divorce was loving and supportive—the best single mom anyone could ever ask for. She was intuitive and so well-spoken. Shari never regretted her parents' divorce.

Fortunately, after years of maturation her father stopped drinking completely and became a pillar of stability for their family. Her parents never remarried but they were obviously friends and parented as a unit. Shari thought this was wonderful and she felt blessed to have amazing parents who were unfortunately better apart than together. Of course, she was not aware of the struggle her parents went through to come to this place of peace between them. They did not involve her in their challenges.

Shari's phone rang and she jumped. It was her mother. "Good morning, Mom. How are you this fine Saturday?"

Her mother, smiling through the phone, said, "Honey, I am doing great. How do you feel about meeting for lunch today?"

Shari was excited and said, "Of course...I would love to see you. Are you in town now?"

"Yes, I am at the bed and breakfast down the street. I needed to be nearby for a business meeting and didn't want to miss the opportunity to see you while I was here." Shari thought it was odd that she didn't tell her in advance she was coming to town. Her mother had left this small town after Shari graduated from high school. She said she needed a change and a new perspective on life. She moved to a beautiful town just a couple of hours away but they didn't get to see each other as much as they wanted.

"Do you want to come here for lunch? They have an amazing menu."

Shari agreed eagerly and said, "Yes, I'll see you at half past eleven?" Her mother agreed and Shari hung up the phone. She smiled a big smile and said to herself, "I wonder what that's about?" She shrugged and headed off to take a shower.

Shari arrived at the B & B at eleven thirty on the dot. Her mother was sitting on the patio and motioned to her to come on over to the table. She hugged Shari so deeply that she thought her bones would break. "Mom, wow. Did you miss me?"

Her mom laughed and sat down. "Here, have a seat, tell me all about what's been going on in your world. I feel like you have not been sharing things with me. Are you doing well?"

Shari had a funny feeling this was why her mom was in town. How dare she ambush her like this? A little voice in the back of Shari's mind said, "Whoa, girl. Hang on a minute. Why are you feeling ambushed? Take a breath. This is your mom. She loves you more than life."

Shari took in a deep breath just the way her mom had taught her to do many years ago and let it out slowly. Five, four, three, two, one. She could feel her heart rate slowing down and her agitation decreasing. The voice in her head said, "Ahh, yes that's better." Why was she suddenly hearing this voice? She had not heard it in so long. She actually thought the voice, her intuition, had abandoned her. It was comforting and unnerving at the same time.

Her mom noticed her uncomfortable demeanor and said, "OK, I am so sorry to shock you. Apparently you have some things going on I didn't know about. I can see it on your face."

The B & B hostess appeared quietly at their table and said, "I brought you a pitcher of water. Lunch is ready on the table over there. Please help yourself to as much as you like. There is plenty." She then winked at Shari's mom and smiled a big welcoming smile and walked away as quietly as she appeared.

Shari wiggled in her seat and said, "Let's get some food and I'll fill you in."

Shari and her mother had an amazing lunch. She did fill her in on everything that had been going on and her mother kindly nodded and smiled. She never interrupted her. She allowed her to get it all out before she asked a single question. She could see Shari's body relax slowly and she knew she had made the right decision to come without telling her first.

There was no business meeting. She just wanted to spend time with her daughter with no expectations of how it would be. When Shari stopped talking her mom reached across the table and took her hand in both of her hands and looked her directly in the eyes. "Shari, I want to apologize to you for not being the mother you needed as a child. I know that I was not as available emotionally as I should have been."

Shari shook her head in disbelief. "Mom. No. You were an amazing mother to me. My current situation is my fault. I got too excited and wanted to be that person so badly I didn't see the red flags until it was too late."

Her mom, Rosalee, smiled a meek but loving smile. "I think there are some things you need to know about your childhood that may help you make sense of how you are feeling now. Have you ever heard of generational curses or for lack of a better term, *sins of the father?*" Shari's eyes got big and she started to say something to defend her father but was curious where this was going so she decided to listen instead.

Her mom saw her expression change and said, "Hear me out." Shari nodded and leaned forward to be sure to take in everything her mother was preparing to say.

Rosalee took a sip of water and began. "Shari, you don't remember this but when you were very small, your father and I had a very tumultuous relationship. We were young and headstrong. Neither of us was good at communication or regulating our emotions. We both have learned so much over the years but I feel like your ability to self-regulate was molded by those experiences. Even if you don't exactly remember them." Her mom leaned back in her chair and closed her eyes for a second. She took a deep breath and let it out slowly, just as she had taught Shari to do many times.

Shari watched her mom's expression change from tight

and stressed to relaxed and confident in just a few seconds. When Rosalee opened her eyes Shari could tell she was definitely more in tune with her emotions. "I know you are aware of the fighting that went on in our home. What you are not aware of is the mental abuse that we endured. I have to take responsibility for my part in this, but I need you to understand it so that you can heal yourself." She nodded as if asking for permission to continue. Shari smiled and nodded back. She reached for her mother's hand and held it gently.

Rosalee continued. "Have you ever heard of the term *gaslighting?*" She paused for a reply from Shari. Shari didn't speak, but she shook her head no. "Gaslighting is a term used to explain how someone manipulates your thoughts in such a way that it makes you doubt your own sanity. Sometimes it appears as a backhanded compliment. You know the type. You've heard a comment such as, 'You look good, for your age.' It sounds like a compliment but it doesn't feel like one.

Another example is an accusation of something you did not do, in an effort to start a fight that can be turned around and then you end up apologizing to the person. Even things like 'I never said that' or 'you must have a bad memory' can be considered gaslighting. Your father used this tactic on me so many times, I literally felt like I was losing my memory and my mind. It's the reason I sometimes seemed like I was unhinged during an argument. He would quietly gaslight me in ways that were so sneaky that I would eventually snap and lose it. Then he would act like I was crazy and storm off leaving me in an emotional state. I was so wrecked that I could not manage my own emotions.

It was during these times you would try to console me and I would send you to your room to spare you the details of my situation. I see now that was wrong. I thought I was protecting you from the drama and chaos but now I know better. I left you alone and confused. I am sure you were sad and lonely in your room wondering what you did to cause all of this pain. It wasn't you. It was never your fault. You were such a kind and loving child. My biggest fear at that time was forcing you to grow up too fast by facing these adult issues. I am so sorry that I handled things so poorly for you." Her mother took a deep breath and carefully dabbed a tear at the corner of her eye with her napkin. She blinked hard and sighed while looking intently at Shari.

Shari took that as her cue to speak. "Mom. Please don't be so hard on yourself."

Rosalee interrupted her and said, "Honey, I have forgiven myself for not knowing. My goal is to educate you so that you can avoid this generational pattern. Break the cycle so to speak."

Shari leaned forward and said, "Generational cycle?" Her brow was deeply furrowed and she was intently looking into her mother's eyes for some clue as to what that meant, exactly.

Rosalee smiled and said, "It's not that serious. Smile, sweetheart. We all do the best we can. 'Once we know better, we do better,' is my favorite quote by Maya Angelou. That's what I am doing here. I am trying to do better by you."

Shari smiled and looked lovingly at her mother. "OK, Mom. I hear you. I can totally relate to that gaslighting term. I didn't tell you that I went to see a trauma expert a couple times. She has a group on Wednesdays, also. It's been eye-opening to say the least. I am going to ask her about this also."

Rosalee smiled and said, "I am so glad you are talking to

someone. My goal was to open your eyes to the sneaky ways abuse comes into your life. I want you to be able to recognize it and avoid it when you can. Toxic humans exist in every walk of life. They are very good at looking normal on the outside. They can be charming, loving and completely adorable and supportive until they get you behind closed doors. It's common for them to try to isolate you from your friends and family so that no one can see what's happening. They want you to use them as your only support system. This way they can manipulate everything in your life."

Shari froze. Her eyes were wide and she was not even breathing. Suddenly her heart was racing and she felt like she was going to scream. She took in a rapid breath and held it. Rosalee recognized this sign immediately and said to her beloved daughter. "Breath out slowly. I am so sorry that I triggered something inside of you. Are you OK?"

Shari took a sip of water and thought for a minute. She needed courage to say what was going to come out next. "Mom, that's exactly how I felt. In the beginning I was flattered that he wanted to spend every waking minute with me. I thought it was how a real relationship was supposed to be. He seemed so loving and nurturing and so involved in my life. I thought it was normal. I thought he loved me." She stopped suddenly and turned green. "Oh no. I think I might vomit."

Rosalee reached across the table and grabbed her hand. "Breathe, Shari. That's it. Let it out slowly. Feeling better?" Shari nodded slowly, wondering why she had such a guttural response to their conversation.

Her mom smiled and said, "OK, I think that's enough for now. How are you feeling?"

Shari said, "Better. Mom, I am so interested in this conversation but I feel wrung out, like I need a nap now.

Can we talk again later today? I want to do this but I feel overwhelmed."

Rosalee stood up and Shari followed her lead. They embraced in a long, comforting hug. "Honey, I am at your disposal. I want you to be OK. I want you to live an amazing and happy life, but I feel like this is a conversation you need to have in order to do that."

Shari nodded and smiled sheepishly. "I agree. I feel like this is the right path for me to be on. It's like my guardian angel has started talking to me again. It's been so long since I heard that calming voice. How do I encourage it to continue?"

Rosalee smiled a big, knowing smile and whispered in her daughter's ear. "Just listen. It's always been there but the chaos was too loud for you to hear it. I'm so excited for you to be on the road to recovery. I hope you can forgive us. I have forgiven your father and myself for our part in the chaos we created between us. It would be easy to blame him for it, but I know that my lack of boundaries and conditioning from my own childhood prevented me from standing strong against his aggression. Your father has his own demons to process but he has made some massive shifts in the last fifteen years. My only concern now is to break this generational pattern before we pass it on to our grandchildren."

Shari leaned back and said, "Oh you had to go there, didn't you." Then she laughed out loud and said, "OK, Mom. I am going to go for a walk and we can chat later. Would you like to get together for dinner this evening?"

Her mom kissed her cheek gently and said, "I'd love that."

Shari did just that. She headed to the park down the street and walked and walked and walked. She felt more and more calm the longer she walked even though her mind was still racing. "How many times had he done that to me? The gaslighting thing my mom explained. Why have I never heard of this before? Is it common?" There were so many questions and not enough answers. Shari felt really good about it though. She felt like things were starting to make sense. She truly felt like she was beginning to find the pathway back to her old self but with new tools and a new outlook.

15 HIM

Shari forgot that he was in town that weekend. She was so focused on the conversation she had with her mother she did not hear the footsteps behind her until she felt the hand on her shoulder. She spun around fully expecting it to be Lily or Leo or even her mom. It wasn't though. It was him. She opened her mouth to scream for help and his hand was over her mouth so quickly and fiercely she could feel her teeth cutting into her lips. His hands were so big and strong that he partially covered her nose as well and she could not take in a breath easily. She wiggled and fought him and he whispered in her ear through clenched teeth, "Stop fighting and I'll let go."

Shari felt her body go limp. Her natural reaction to flee had left her. She was now paralyzed and numb. He felt her body relax and he let go of her mouth slowly. He turned her to look at him and said with disgust. "I can't believe you made me do that, Shari. I only want to talk to you. Why do you always make me do things I don't want to do? It hurts me to see you hurt."

Shari's mind was racing again. How could he say that? She did nothing to him. How is this situation her fault in any way? Then she heard the voice. It was only one word. Gaslighting. She stood up straight and gathered her wits. "What do you want?" she asked with a stern voice. She hoped that being stern would deter him from whatever nefarious scheme he was planning.

He looked at her with tears in his eyes and said, "Shari, you know I love you. Why are you so determined to hurt me?"

She stepped back in shock. "What?" she said quietly. "We haven't seen each other in so long. How am I hurting you? I thought you were over me since you have a new girlfriend."

He threw his head back and laughed as if she had said the funniest thing in the history of jokes. "She's nobody to me. Just some girl I met at the bar. I don't want her, I want you." Shari's mind started to come back into reality from the shock of it all and she realized they were alone on the walking trail. She scanned her surroundings to see if there was anyone around to call out for help and saw no one.

She decided it was best not to antagonize him. She tried to start walking toward the parking lot and he grabbed her arm firmly. "Where are you going?" he said sharply.

Shari nodded toward her car and said, "I'm supposed to meet my mom and I'm late. Walk with me, please." She prayed that getting closer to her car would make her safer. Maybe someone would pull into the parking lot or she could dodge him and run for the car. He walked with her slowly, holding her arm like she was a prisoner.

She said again, "Tom, I'm late and my mother will be looking for me if I don't arrive on time. I need to go. Can we talk later?"

He stopped her abruptly and said, "No, we are going to talk now. Don't you think I can see through your lies?"

She wasn't really telling a lie. She did fib a little about

what time her mother would start to be concerned but she stood firm in her story. "I'm not lying, Tom." She hated saying his name out loud. It felt like spitting venom. Just then a truck pulled into the parking lot and she jerked her elbow out of his grasp and made a dash for her car. He didn't dare follow her, but she knew this wasn't the last of his antics.

She locked the door and quickly drove out of the lot. She went straight to the bed and breakfast and found her mother sitting on the back deck sipping tea.

Her mother saw her coming and recognized the look of horror on her face and got up to meet her with a big hug. "Honey, what happened? What's got you so scared?" Shari collapsed on the nearest patio chair and sobbed. It was the first time she had allowed herself to really cry. Her mother sat in silence until her daughter stopped shaking and handed her a tissue. "Are you alright? Are you hurt?" She was looking her over for bruises or any signs of a struggle.

"No, Mom, I'm OK. I'm not hurt physically. He did cover my mouth to keep me from screaming but otherwise it was just words." She winced as she realized her lip was cut from her teeth on the inside. No one could see it though so she chose not to speak of it.

She recounted the event to her mother in great detail, stopping to blow her nose and wipe a tear from time to time. "Why won't he leave me alone?" she cried out loud. "I just want to move on with my life." She leaned over and put her head on her mother's shoulder. "I'm so glad you are here," she whispered.

Just at that moment her phone dinged and it was a text from him. It read "Shari, I can't believe you think I want you back. You are nothing to me. Please leave me and my new girlfriend alone. She doesn't deserve to be dragged into your drama. STAY AWAY FROM US!"

Shari handed the phone to her mom and said, "He's insane. How can he twist things like this? He came up to me. He threatened me. How can he possibly think this is OK?"

Her mom shook her head in knowing disbelief. "He's covering his tracks, honey. He needs his new girlfriend to believe that you are the problem. It's part of his manipulation of her. It's sick but it's all a show."

Shari looked back up at her mother and suddenly remembered something. "Oh my God. He did this to me too. I remember now. He used to tell me his ex was so abusive to him and would not leave him alone. He would show me text messages from her and tell me she was crazy all the time. It all makes sense now. I am so glad I never replied to him. He has no texts from me to show this poor woman.

Mom, I saw her the other day and she looked so down. She literally looks like someone who has no will to live. She reminded me of myself a year ago. I felt so bad for her but I didn't know what to do about it. As a matter of fact she may have texted me the other day." Shari looked through her phone and found the text from the stranger. She showed it to her mother.

Rosalee frowned and looked deeply into Shari's eyes. "Honey, she is not your responsibility. Reaching out to her will only cause more pain and chaos in your life. I know you want to save her from him but as you can see it's not that easy. She has to make her own decision. Anything you say to her will come back to hurt you times ten. Please take my advice and stay out of their relationship. No good will come of this." Shari nodded and based on his actions earlier in the day she agreed with her mother. She wanted nothing more than to never, ever see him again.

Rosalee decided it was not safe to go to the restaurant

they were planning to visit for dinner because he was obviously watching her. She understood that getting a restraining order may sound like a good idea but was terrified of the ramifications of taking that sort of action against this obviously unhinged man. She suggested they get some takeout and watch a movie that evening at the bed and breakfast.

Shari agreed and said, "I want to go home and change and wash my face. If you call in some food, I can stop and pick it up on my way back."

Rosalee agreed and walked Shari to her car. "Please be careful, honey. I'll see you soon."

Shari drove home carefully, watching to be sure she wasn't being followed. She remembered that Leo's friend was going to teach her some self-defense tomorrow and she was ready for that. She wondered if she should tell Leo about what had happened. She decided not to. Surely he doesn't want to be with a woman who has so much drama in her life?

She made it home unscathed. Shari carefully searched her surroundings to be sure no one was watching and slipped into Lily's house. She went straight to the shower and climbed in, letting the hot water rain down on her body. The steam rising and sticking to the glass doors felt so good. "Thank God for instant water heaters. I can stay in here all day and never run out of hot water," she thought.

When she finally emerged from the steamy shower her skin was red and blotchy. She carefully caressed her skin with the best smelling lotion and stared at her face in the mirror. She brushed her teeth carefully because her lips were extremely sore. She could not see any noticeable swelling though so she was relieved. She heard the voice in her head say, "Why are you still covering for him?" Shari shrugged and thought it was best not to make trouble.

She found her most comfy clothes for movie night with her mom and dressed quietly. She felt exhausted and sad. Almost depressed. She hated feeling this way. A week ago she was cheerful and excited about life and now she felt like the despair was grappling for her attention again.

16 SELF-DEFENSE

Shari woke early Sunday and was excited to see Leo and learn some self-defense from his lifelong friend. She texted him first thing and asked, "What time should I come over today?" She knew he had told her but she could not remember for the life of her what he said. It was like her memory was failing her. For a brief moment she recalled him saying to her, "You don't know what happened. Your memory sucks!" Maybe he was right. Maybe her memory was bad. Leo replied, "One o'clock. You don't need to bring anything except your beautiful smile." Shari replied with a blushing emoji.

When Shari arrived at Leo's house it was a few minutes after one. She felt like she was always showing up early at his house and didn't want to seem too eager. Also, with the events of yesterday still fresh in her mind she didn't want him asking her any questions that might cause her to cry. She really just wanted to forget the whole thing. His friends were already there and she breathed a sigh of relief. She made her way to the front door and it opened before she got there. "Welcome," said Leo as he bowed upon her entry. He chuckled and said, "I saw you parking so I thought I would greet you like a princess." She smiled at the silliness and was happy to have a lighter mood.

They barbecued and talked with his friend Dale and his wife about all sorts of unimportant topics and it was a refreshing afternoon. After the meal was cleaned up his friend Dale clapped his hands together and said, "You ready to learn some self-defense?"

Shari stood up and said, "I am. Let's do this." She shrugged and said to him, "Apparently my memory is awful though so you may have to repeat yourself."

Dale stopped and looked her in the eyes with concern and said, "Who told you that?"

Shari blinked and looked back at him in shock. "What? That my memory is bad?" He nodded.

She replied, "Well it seems to be. My ex used to tell me all the time I didn't remember things correctly. I think maybe he is right."

Dale stopped and pulled out a barstool and said, "Here have a seat. I want to explain something to you." Shari sat carefully on the barstool and looked him square in the eyes. She was obviously curious as to what he was going to say next. "Shari, I have only known you for a few hours but let me make this absolutely clear to you. Nothing he ever said to you was true. I would venture to guess it may have been true about him, but not you. He projected his own insecurities onto you and he deliberately made you feel inferior and incapable of taking care of yourself on purpose.

"If your memory is bad, it could be that your short-term memory is suffering from overexposure to cortisol. Do you know what cortisol is?" Shari nodded. "When you are in a stressful and toxic situation—it could be a relationship or work, for example—the constantly high level of cortisol can damage your short-term memory. Don't worry though. I doubt it's permanent. The longer you are safe and relaxed the better your memory will be. Is that helpful?"

Shari stood up and said, "Yes. I am so glad you explained that to me. It makes so much sense. Let's do this." She followed Dale outside to the backyard and listened intently to what he had to say. He showed her several ways to escape a hold and explained how she needed to be aware in all situations. She thought to herself, "This would have been good information yesterday."

He also said, "Muscle memory is something you need to make these moves solid. You want them to happen without needing to think. It's not your short-term memory that you need for this. I would guess that Leo would be happy to help you practice this until it becomes instinctive so you won't need to rely on your memory." Leo smiled and nodded eagerly.

The afternoon was a success. Shari felt safer already. She could tell that Leo was anxious to help her learn the moves as well. He was such a nice man. Dale and his wife had to go pick up their children so they headed toward the door. Leo and Shari walked to the door with them and Leo put his arm around Shari as they said goodbye. Normally Shari would have moved away from his embrace but this time she welcomed it. It felt warm and safe to be there in that place with him.

After the door closed she turned toward him and leaned in for a kiss. He was happy to comply and hugged her tightly for what felt like a long time right there by the door. He leaned back and said, "You don't have to go yet do you?" She shook her head no and he turned and led her back to the couch. They sat down and he turned on a movie. She didn't even look to see what the title was. She was content to sit near him on the couch and say nothing. For the first time in a long time she felt safe and happy. He held her hand and stroked her hair lovingly. She snuggled up under his arm and pretended to pay attention to the movie but she was completely unaware of what was happening on the screen. She was just taking in this moment and enjoying her brief feelings of happiness. She didn't even realize that she fell asleep.

She woke suddenly when Leo moved. He looked at her and said, "I'm sorry. I need to close up the barbecue pit and tidy up the backyard. You can stay right here and sleep if you want."

Shari rubbed her eyes and stood up. "No. I am so sorry I fell asleep. It's been a long weekend. I should probably go home. Thank you so much for everything."

Leo smiled and pulled her in for another hug. He looked deep into her eyes and said, "It's no problem at all. I really enjoy spending time with you. I am so glad you are learning self-defense and I am happy to help you practice any time. As long as you don't use it on me." He winked at her and smiled that warm smile she was becoming so used to seeing. He gently pressed his lips against hers and said, "I'll walk you to your car."

Shari drove home in a trance. She was shocked that her day went so well. She felt a little guilty for not telling Leo about Saturday but decided there was plenty of time for that. She climbed into bed and slept better than she had in a very long time.

She was learning to trust Leo. It felt good to trust someone but she was so cautious. Feeling safe with someone was going to be a long journey for her. Not only was she having trouble trusting others, but she felt like she could not trust her own judgment, especially when it comes to men. How can she really know if they are faking it? She knew that time was going to be her best friend in this area. She was glad that Leo appeared to be OK with going slow.

17 THE REAL LEO

Shari made it through the first part of the week well. She was excited to go to the group session on Wednesday and she had been feeling so confident and secure after spending the day with Leo on Sunday that she was totally caught off guard when one of the attendees of the group's story hit her square in the gut.

She was sitting near the hallway to the restrooms with her back to the doors sipping a hot tea and listening intently to everyone's stories. She could smell the peppermint in the tea and was enjoying the cooling effect of it going down her throat and was musing about how something warm could also feel cool.

A small framed woman about Shari's age was sharing about her last relationship and one of the things her ex loved to do to torment her. She explained that he would deliberately move things in the house from where she had placed them, and sit back and watch her frantically look for them. He would ask questions as if he was trying to help, but he was actually just gearing up to make her feel stupid. In the example she was sharing she had spent 2 hours looking for her car keys.

She had already missed the appointment she had to meet with a friend for lunch. She called her friend and apologized to let her know she was not going to be able to make it. When she hung up the phone with tears in her eyes he smirked at her and said "Did you look in the bedroom night stand?" Deflated, she explained that she would never put her keys in the bedroom. They should be in her purse, or at worst laying next to her purse in the foyer of the house, near the front door. His response was "Suit yourself." With a shrug. He then went into the kitchen and she made her way to the bedroom to see if maybe he was right.

As she opened the top drawer to her night stand he slammed the bedroom door open so hard it hit the wall with a big bang and she jumped. She went on to describe how her heart felt like it jumped into her throat and she instantly felt sick. He shoved past her and reached into the drawer and pulled out the keys and threw them at her. Shouting "I told you they were in there. I don't know why you just don't listen to me!" She showed the scar on her collarbone from where the keys hit her and made a gash. She had to get 4 stitches because it bled and would not stop.

As she was finishing her story, Shari was no longer listening. She could hear the voice but it sounded so far away. Her hands were shaking so hard she had to put the tea down. She started sweating and she could feel her breath speeding up. She was feeling more and more uncomfortable and was beginning to wonder if she was going to pass out when someone placed a cold rag on the back of her neck and stooped down next to her and looked her in the eyes. "Shari, are you ok?" The far away voice said kindly. "Do you need to lie down?" Shari blinked hard and put all of her effort into focusing on the person in front of her. As she started to come back to the room she could hear her now friend and counselor saying breathe, slowly, in and out. You are safe right now."

Shari started to realize what had happened and she was instantly embarrassed. Her mind started racing. How could I interrupt someone else's time like that? How inconsiderate of me! She started to apologize but the small woman came immediately to her side and apologized to Shari for upsetting her. A few more deep breaths and Shari started to feel more normal. "What was that?" She asked.

Mel smiled softly and said "I think you were having a panic attack, or at least feeling very anxious. Is there something you would like to share with the group?" Shari thought deeply for a minute. She took in the sounds in the room. She could hear a fan running and what sounded like a train off in the distance. She could smell the tea and the faint smell of coffee on Mels breath. She could feel her breathing becoming more steady and she gently shook her head no. "I honestly don't know what caused that to happen."

Mel squeezed her hand and said "something in her story must have triggered a deep emotion or memory for you. You don't recall anything similar happening to you? Or maybe just feeling how she must have felt in that moment?" Shari nodded. "Oh, yes, her story seems so familiar to me. Of course it's not the same but I can totally relate to how she must have felt in that moment."

Mel gently hugged her and asked if she wanted her to call Leo or Lily to come get her. She didn't think that Shari should drive after that experience. To her own surprise Shari nodded in agreement. "Thank you, I will call Leo myself." She got up and went toward the bathrooms and dialed Leo's number.

Leo answered immediately. "Hey, sweetie. I thought you had group tonight? Is everything ok?" Shari paused. Took in a deep breath and said "No, actually. I sort of had a melt down. Can I bother you to come and pick me up? Mel doesn't want me to drive right now." Leo immediately said, "Of course, I am on my way. I will be there in 10."

Shari went into the restroom so that she could splash some cold water on her face. She looked in the mirror and was shocked at how she looked. Her skin was all blotchy and her neck was red. She looked disheveled. "Listen Shari! You have 10 minutes to pull yourself together!" She said to her reflection. Unfortunately it was going to take a lot longer than that.

Ten minutes later Leo swept in like a spring breeze, stopped to say hi to Mel and get a brief update then headed to the restroom under her direction. He knocked on the door lightly and asked "Shari, are you OK?" Shari opened the door and smiled sheepishly. She was embarrassed that she had called him to come to her rescue but she really just wanted to be wrapped in his warm embrace and forget what happened.

She stepped out of the restroom and grabbed her jacket off the coat rack and allowed Leo to wrap his arm around her shoulder. Together they walked in silence. Leo winked at Mel on the way by and opened the door to let Shari step through. As he helped her into the passenger seat he could tell that she was about to lose her composure again. He leaned in and gave her a quick hug and said "Your place or mine?" Shari whispered one word before the tears started flowing. "Yours."

Leo drove to his house and pulled the truck into the garage. He quickly made his way around to her side of the truck and helped her out. He handed her a tissue and guided her into the house. As she sat on the couch he pointed towards the wine rack and she nodded. While he poured a glass of wine she pulled herself together enough to be able to speak again. She whispered "Thank you, " as he sat down next to her. He sat silently with her until she was ready to speak. He was content just being there for her while she was obviously processing some deep emotions.

Shari took in a long ragged breath and let it out slowly. She looked up at Leo's concerned face and chuckled a little bit. He raised an eyebrow but didn't say a word. Shari took a small sip of wine and said "I am so embarrassed for you to see me this way, but honestly I am glad to be here with you right now. I know I have not told you much about my past relationship. Something happened at group tonight that made me come apart at the seams. I can't even tell you exactly what it was. I just felt so moved by her story and it felt so real to me that I got overwhelmed."

Leo leaned in and hugged her softly. "Shari, I know you have some healing to do and I am happy to be here to support you in any way I can. What can I do for you right now?" Shari smiled at him and said. "You are doing it. Just hold me, please." Leo was happy to comply with her request. They sat for over an hour just snuggled up on the couch together. He could slowly feel the tension melting off of her and he was so glad to be able to be there for her.

Shari looked at Leo with deeply furrowed brows and asked "Would it be alright if I explained some of the details of my past relationship to you? I feel like maybe if you knew what I went through you may be able to support me better. I don't want to be one of those girls that sits around and talks about her ex all the time though." Leo softly laughed and said "Of course, you can tell me anything and I already know that is not the type of girl you are. I would be honored if you trust me with your journey. I will never hold anything that happened to you in the past against the person you are now.

Shari sighed deeply, then a big, thankful, smile slowly shaped itself on her lips. For the next hour she filled him in on everything she could think of about that time in her life. How he treated her, how she perceived it all and how she felt so stupid for falling for his games. She explained her mothers confession about how she felt responsible for her lack of boundaries due to her own relationship issues. She didn't leave anything out.

When she was done, Leo smiled and gave her a big hug. "Shari, thank you so much for sharing all of that with me. I promise to cherish and protect those memories. How would you feel if I filled you in on some things about my life, since we are on the topic?

Shari blinked and said "What? You had a life before you met me? HA! Well, yes it would be a great distraction from my current mood. Please fill me in."

Leo leaned back and sighed rather loudly. "Do you need more wine before I start my story?" Shari shook her head no and said "No way. You are not getting out of this that easy." They both laughed and got a little more comfortable on the couch.

Leo started by saying "I have to tell you. I am no angel. I have had my share of problems with relationships and with my parents as well." He paused to see if she was still on board. Shari was staring at him so intently she just nodded excitedly. "OK Here goes then. I have to admit I am a little jealous of your family. It sounds like you have amazing parents. Mine on the other hand is a bit of a hot mess.

My parents are still married, but they have had their share of ups and downs. At one point my dad actually moved out of the house. I am not sure but I think my parents went to marriage counseling. They never spoke of it but it was obvious to me that they did work hard to save their marriage. As a child there was no calm in my house. It was utter chaos on the daily. We woke up to a screaming mom, telling us to get our butts out of bed and get ready for school. She had one level of volume and it was all the way up. All of us spent a lot of time trying to avoid her moods. She would not like me to share this with you but she was abused as a child and she had a very hard time regulating herself when she was stressed.

The biggest issue was that she was extremely unorganized, moody and had severe abandonment issues. She did great when she had a full time job, or at least she seemed to but when dad asked her to stay home with us kids, I guess her consistency went out the window and lots of chaos happened because of it. I learned years later that being a workaholic and super organized was a coping strategy she had adopted. When she stopped working to stay home with us it really affected her in a bad way.

As a child I was extremely shy due to this. I was also embarrassed to go anywhere with her because she would lose it in public places. She would yell at the supermarket people or fight over a parking space. For many years I just tried to never go anywhere with her. She was better at home but if my dad or us kids did anything to upset her there was hell to pay. God forbid we break something or spill something on her super clean floors."

He stopped to take a sip of wine and chuckled a little. Shari smiled and waited for him to continue. She was shocked to hear this about his family because he seemed so self assured and normal!

"Eventually, my mom found a therapist who really helped her. She learned about what had happened to her as a child and the effects it had on her body and mental state as an adult. She became so passionate about it that she went back to school to become a psychiatrist. She literally changed everything about herself as I was growing up. The best thing about it was that she shared what she was learning with me. I guess because I was curious and I would sit and listen to her talk for hours. I would help her with her homework and we would have deep discussions about what she was earning.

Honestly, I am surprised that I didn't end up following in her footsteps, but I just love working outdoors and my landscaping jobs allow me to use my creativity. I am who I am today because I watched my mom go through all of that. I watched her grow emotionally and I watched them heal their marriage and our family by doing what they did together. I am truly blessed to have experienced that as a young adult. I fully believe that if she had not started school when she did that we would all still be a mess."

Shari smiled and said "Wow, I had no idea. I guess you have a really good relationship with your mother now?" Leo smiled and said "The best! As a matter of fact, I would love for you to meet her but I didn't want to rush you." Shari smiled and said "She sounds amazing. I would be honored to meet her."

18 FAMILY

The next few weeks flew by. Shari and Leo were spending more time together. She heard nothing from Tom at all. Secretly she hoped he had moved on and would never bother her again but she had her doubts. Leo was diligent in reminding her to practice her self-defense moves. She teased him that he only liked it because he got to grab her from behind. She was fierce and her skills were becoming automatic just like Dale said they would. Leo was learning not to sneak up on her as well. She had extremely sharp elbows and she wasn't afraid to use them.

Leo had arranged for Shari to meet his parents. They all went to eat at this quaint little restaurant and the food was amazing but the company was extraordinary. His parents were truly kind and accepting of Shari. His mom Angie was adorable and so sweet. She sat right next to Shari and asked her all kinds of questions about her job and her family.

Leo's dad Joe was tall and handsome and loved to pass out big bear hugs. Shari accepted one of his famous hugs immediately. He felt so fatherly and safe and smelled like spiced rum. His laugh would warm a room and she could see a lot of him in Leo. It was amazing spending time with his family and his mom made sure to let her know that she expected to see her at thanksgiving for a meal she would never forget. Shari accepted with a smile and agreed it would be fun to spend Thanksgiving with his family.

As Shari climbed into the truck and Leo closed the door she saw her mother and father across the street in the same car. She waved big at them and they came over to the truck window. Shari asked "What are the two of you up to?" Her dad snickered and winked at her while her mom looked a little nervous. Rosalee said " Well, honestly we are shopping for a Christmas present for you." Shari smiled and said "What is it? Tell me, tell me, tell me! She clapped with each word and bounced in the seat. "You know I hate surprises. Just tell me what it is."

Leo had walked back around the truck to shake her fathers hand and said "Don't you dare tell her." With a chuckle. Frank grabbed Leos hand and pumped it like a well handle. "Nice to finally meet you. You. Must be Leo." "Yessir" said Leo. "It's so nice to meet you too!" Rosalee took that moment to throw her arms around Leo's neck and hug him tightly. She was much shorter than him so her feet came off the ground. After he hugged her with a famous bear hug and put her down they all laughed.

"Frank said, "Hey, would you two like some ice cream? We are going to stop in that little shop before we go shopping. It would be great if you joined us." Shari opened the truck door and said, "Well, when have I ever said no to ice cream? Leo, you in?" He bowed like a prince and said, "After you, m'lady." They walked hand in hand to the ice cream shop. She bumped him and whispered. "Both families in the same day!" He winked at her and said, " I think it's great."

The little ice cream shop had a small table for 4 so they grabbed it right away and sent the boys to the counter to get sundaes. Rosalee leaned over to Shari and said, "What were you two doing?" Shari smiled a big cheesy grin and said, "I got to meet Leo's parents tonight. They are lovely. Oh, and what are you two really up to? Don't tell me you're Christmas shopping. It's not even Thanksgiving yet." Rosalee smiled and said, "Your father and I get together now and then just to catch up. It's nice having him as a friend. We have so many things in common, namely you. Sometimes it's just easier to talk to him than someone else."

Shari raised her eyebrows and asked, "Is everything OK?" Her mom responded with "Of course. I am so glad we ran into you. I am excited to meet Leo." Shari was not sure that there wasn't more to her story but she didn't want to push her mom so she let it go. For now.

Leo and Frank came back with ice cream so they all sat and chatted and filled their bellies with delicious sundaes. Leo told her dad that she was learning self defense and was shocked. "My little girl! I am so proud of you for doing that. Have you had to use any of your new skills yet?" They all chuckled and he eyed Shari curiously. She shook her head no but said with cheer, " I have really sharp elbows though…Just ask Leo!" He nodded emphatically. "That she does," he said.

As they were walking back to the truck Leo leaned towards Shari and asked: "Hey, do you think we could invite both of our parents over to the house for dinner? I bet they would really get along. Shari thought for a minute and said, "What about we invite them all over and do Thanksgiving at your house?" Leo shrugged and said, "Well, my mom usually does a big spread but I bet we could do that. I will ask her tomorrow."

As they climbed back into the truck Shari couldn't help but feel loved. What a great evening. She got to meet his parents and they were both amazing and he got to meet her parents. Even though she was still suspicious as to why they were together." She leaned back in the seat and hooked her seatbelt with a big smile on her face.

Several days passed and Shari suddenly got a text from Angie. "Hey Shari, Leo invited us over for Thanksgiving and I am thrilled to do it at his home. Are you also inviting your parents? We would love to meet them?" Shari responded with an emphatic YES, they are looking forward to meeting you both, too." Angie replied, "Great. Tell them not to bring anything because between me and Leo there will be plenty to go around. We both love to cook! See you Thursday!"

Thursday arrived so quickly. Their multi-family dinner went amazing. Everyone had a great time, and Angie was right, the food was plentiful and so very good. Leo really knows how to throw a party Shari thought to herself. It felt so great to be with people who she felt she could trust. She was also becoming very comfortable at Leo's house. So much so that when the second bottle of wine was opened she decided that she would be staying the night.

Everyone worked together to clean up as a team and it was so much fun. The house was back to normal in no time. Leo went outside to get some logs for the fireplace and came back in with a huge Christmas tree. Rosalee and Angie both were giddy with excitement. While Joe, Frank and Leo got the tree prepped for decorations, the ladies found the ornaments and started organizing. Shari made some of Leo's special hot chocolate for the group and found a Christmas station on the radio and the whole group set to decorating the tree.

They sang and laughed and took pictures of the tree. It was truly an enjoyable experience. The smell of the real pine tree was so delicious and once the lights were on it looked amazing. Shari was so happy having everyone together for the occasion. She was really starting to look forward to Christmas.

After their families left, Shari flopped down on the couch and said, "I think I'll stay here tonight if it's alright with you." Leo smiled that gorgeous smile of his and flopped down right next to her on the couch. "I would love it if you stayed." "I may never leave," Shari said with a smile. Leo was happy to have her there and offered the spare bedroom. Shari was shocked that he didn't expect her to sleep with him.

Before she could say a word he winked and said, unless you want to sleep in my room. You are welcome to do whatever you like. I promise to be a gentleman. Shari decided the spare room was a great way to handle it. She wanted to be there for breakfast but didn't want to have any regrets. She graciously accepted the spare bedroom and a long t-shirt for pajamas. She kissed Leo goodnight and quietly drifted off to sleep.

19 SLUT

The little town they lived in was busy decorating for Christmas. The sights and sounds of Christmas filled the air. Decorations hung from every lamppost, and every store window was filled with cheer.

Lily and Shari decided to take a whole Saturday to shop for the holiday and since their little town had so many stores downtown around the square they decided to stay local for shopping. The town center had a huge tree lighting ceremony the Saturday before Christmas and they were excited to drink hot chocolate and be there for the event.

They agreed to meet Leo and his friend Stan at four to be sure they had a good seat. The weather was beautiful but crisp. Knee-high boots and a nice long coat made Shari feel warm and comfortable outdoors. She and Lily had arms full of bags from shopping and decided to drop them at the car before the party in the town center. There was Christmas music playing through speakers around the square and the decorations were very festive. Shari was happy. She stopped briefly to look into a store window at her reflection and she thought to herself out loud, "I must be crazy, I think I look younger."

Lily heard her and said emphatically, "Yes, you do. I think it's because your stress level has gone down. Well…and Leo may have something to do with it as well. Happy looks good on you."

Shari smiled and said, "Thank you. It feels good to feel happy again." For the first time in a long time she didn't stop to think about how it could all come apart at the seams in an instant. She had learned so much about herself and what she had been through that she truly felt that she was more in control of her emotions than she had ever been in her life. She knew she could call her mom or dad anytime and discuss her feelings with support and love and her relationship with Leos' mom was blossoming. Of course, Leo was always there too and he was so balanced and level-headed. She truly felt supported.

She stuffed her bags into the trunk and slammed the lid shut. Grabbing Lily by the arm she swung her around and said, "Let's go meet those hotties. I bet Leo already has some spiked hot chocolate ready to go. I am so glad you and Stan hit it off. I love having double dates with you two."

Shari had still been keeping Leo at a distance in some ways even though they had been spending a lot of time together. It wasn't that she didn't like him or want to build a relationship together, she was just enjoying taking her time and not feeling rushed. He seemed OK with their slow pace and never pressured her to do anything she wasn't comfortable with. Her daydreams were starting to be more frequent and they all included some sort of time with him.

He was the first man she had ever dated who was comfortable letting her set the pace. He never made promises he couldn't keep and he certainly never tried to make her feel crazy or stupid.

As a matter of fact, he was supportive in many ways but not over the top like Tom was. "Hmm…I can think of his name now without wanting to spit. That has to be progress," she thought to herself. Smiling, she shook off the thought of him and rounded the corner of the town square to see Leo and Stan exactly where she expected them to be. Right up front with a thermos of hot chocolate with some magical ingredients designed to warm their chilly evening.

Leo saw them coming and waved big, and even though she had already seen them she waved back excitedly. As they approached he handed them both a steaming cup of hot chocolate and said with a wink, "Easy now, that's my special recipe. Don't drink it too fast."

Shari, feeling a little silly winked back at him and said playfully, "And what if I do?"

Leo grinned from ear to ear and whispered into the back of her soft hair, "For you, anything. I'll carry you all the way home if I need to." Shari smiled and leaned into his warm embrace. She could not help but wonder if this was how life was supposed to be.

The rest of the evening went amazingly well. There was a bonfire and so many friends to talk to. They took turns rotating their bodies near the fire to stay warm. The Christmas choir was there and sang several wonderful songs that were so beautiful to listen to. The evening was magical just as it should have been.

When the evening was over the guys walked the girls back to Shari's car. He opened the door for her to get in and saw Lily's face suddenly go from happy to angry in a flash. She said, "Shari, you are never going to believe this. Come over here." Shari and Leo walked around the car to see it had been vandalized. Someone had carved the word slut into the door on the passenger side.

Leo pulled Shari aside and said, "Don't worry, we can fix this." He quickly looked around for someone to be watching them and saw no one. He fully expected to see the culprit watching for a reaction. "Shari, who would do this?" he said slowly.

She had begun to cry and looked up at him and said, "I'm sure it was Tom or one of his cronies. I'm so sorry, Leo. I thought this was over. I should go."

Leo reached down and lifted her chin so that her eyes met his and said, "This is not your fault and you are not going home alone. I'll drive you." He tossed Stan his keys and said, "Follow me to their house, will ya?" Stan nodded in agreement and held the door open for Shari to climb in. He closed the door behind her and said, "Lily, you can ride with me." Stan was not as good at hiding his anger as Leo was. He was red-faced and obviously feeling very protective over the girls.

Leo drove Shari home in silence. Her mind was racing. Why isn't he talking? Is he mad at me? What should I do? She looked up at him and could see the muscles in his face working hard. He was angry. She started to speak and he cut her off in the most calm and soothing voice. "Shari, I am so sorry this is happening to you. I hope you realize you have done nothing to deserve this. I have a friend who has a body shop here in town and I am sure he can fix your door easily. Are you absolutely certain that Tom doesn't know where you live? Maybe you should consider a restraining order."

Shari looked at him sincerely. She admired his strong physique and personality. She adored his calm demeanor no matter what the situation but she could clearly see he was angry. She feared making him more angry and was not sure how to respond. He glanced at her and saw the look of terror on her face. "Don't worry. I've got you. I'll stay on the couch if you want me to. I am concerned he may escalate things." She nodded silently out of fear of saying the wrong thing.

They arrived at Lily's house and all four of them went inside. The guys decided they would stay the night to be sure nothing else happened. Shari went into her bedroom to take a breath. She was in there for several minutes when she heard a light tap on her door. It was Leo. "Can I come in?" he asked. Shari nodded. He walked to her and she fell into his arms, sobbing.

"I'm so sorry, Leo. I didn't mean for this to happen. I completely understand if you never want to see me again."

Leo held her tightly for another minute, then leaned back and raised her chin to his eye level. "Shari, I know we have been seeing each other for a short while now and I've been happy to take things at your pace because I care about you. I am not angry at you. I am angry at whoever did that to your car."

Shari sighed. "Are you sure you aren't angry with me? Your life was drama-free until I came along."

Leo laughed and said, "My life was a complete bore before you came along. You have energized my life. I look forward to seeing your cheerful face and hearing your laugh literally every day. I can't imagine a day without you in it."

Shari smiled and leaned back in for another one of his amazing hugs. "Are you really sure? I have no control over my life at this point and I feel like anyone who comes around me is at risk."

Leo chuckled and softly said, "It is going to take more than that lowlife to run me off, Shari. Now come on. Let's go see what movies are on. Surely we can find something funny to watch. I think I still have some of that magical hot chocolate in the thermos too."

Shari made a step toward the bedroom door and yelled,

"Dibs!" They both headed for the living room where Stan and Lily were already sitting looking at movies to stream on the TV.

Lily looked at Shari and mouthed, "You OK?" Shari nodded and smiled. She meant it too. She really felt like she was OK. For the first time in a really long time, she felt like she was more than OK.

They found an old comedy that seemed interesting and they all sat down to watch.

20 SELF-REGULATION

The next morning Shari rose early. Knowing there were guests on the couch made her a little uneasy and she wanted to let them get back to their lives as soon as possible. She dressed and threw her hair in a bun and wandered down the hallway to the living room to see Leo and Stan sitting on the couch with Lily drinking coffee and talking. Leo stood up and said, "Good morning, sunshine. How did you sleep?"

Shari hugged him and said, "I slept better than I expected. Thank you both for staying the night. How about some breakfast?" Everyone nodded and together they headed to a nearby restaurant. It was one of the oldest buildings in the city and they had amazing breakfast food.

Lily and Stan seemed to be hitting it off pretty well. Shari liked having them to pal around with. After breakfast Leo dropped the girls back off at home and he and Stan took off to get Stan's truck.

Shari flopped down on the couch and said, "I'm just gonna sit here for a while. I need a stress detox."

Lily laughed and said, "I bet you do. I am so sorry a certain someone damaged your car. I know we can't prove who did it but I think it's pretty obvious."

Shari nodded and took in a deep breath. "I wish he would just go away. I don't understand why he won't leave me alone."

Lily grunted and made an ugly face. "He's a miserable person and the only way he feels better is by dragging other people into his misery. It's not your fault. The best thing you can do is not react at all. He's watching for your reaction. He's begging for your attention and you are not going to give it."

Shari agreed. It seemed like she was perfectly correct in her idea. She felt like she had been ignoring him though. She never contacted him. She avoided seeing and speaking to him. Hopefully time would work its wonders on his mind and he'd find someone else to help him feel better.

"Leo said he knows someone who can probably buff those scratches out of the paint. He said they don't look too deep," stated Shari with a shrug. "Honestly, I am not even that upset by it. I feel like it could have been worse."

Lily flipped her head around and looked at Shari. "You should be pissed. Raving mad. I am glad you aren't because there is nothing you can do about it but you should not be numb to this. You can never get so used to being mistreated that you are glad one bad thing was easier than another. That's not a good mindset, Shari."

Shari agreed but what could she do? Nothing was within her control. She was tired of feeling helpless. She remembered learning her self-defense moves, which she was really good at, and smiled. "I'm not defenseless, and it's just a car. I am fine," she thought to herself. Anger was not one of her "go-to" emotions. It was rare that she felt anger. She was more hurt that he would stoop so low to get her attention. She hoped Lily was right and no reply was the best reply.

The sun was peeking through the gloomy winter sky but it felt pretty warm outside so Shari decided to go for a walk. She put on her tennis shoes and headed out for a quick stroll. "I'll clear my head and work off that amazing breakfast," she said to Lily.

Lily nodded and said, "OK. Be safe, I'll see you in a bit." Shari remembered she had an appointment with Mel on Monday this week and she was eager to get her input on this situation.

The rest of the day was relaxing and Shari took the downtime to get some laundry done. She sat down to make some notes for her visit with Mel while the dryer was running the last load of laundry.

Monday morning was easy as pie. Shari arrived at work in a fairly cheerful mood even while driving a car that said slut on the side. She received a text from Leo saying his friend would be stopping by later that day to look at her door. She replied with the approximate location of her car in the lot and went back to work. "See, it's all going to be fine," she thought to herself.

Lunchtime came and she was off to visit with Mel. She was excited to walk to her office in the sun even though it was chilly out.

Mel was ready for her when she walked in. She said, "Good afternoon, Shari! How are you today?"

Shari smiled and said, "You know what? I am starting to feel better. I still feel like I should not trust myself or anyone for that matter though. Oh and my car was vandalized this weekend."

Mel stopped sipping her coffee and said, "What? Your car was vandalized? Do you know by whom?"

Shari shook her head no, then said, "I assume I know who it was but I have no proof. Leo thinks it can be buffed out. It was a scratch on the door. The word *slut*."

Mel put her coffee cup down and said, "Well, I guess we do know who did that. I am glad you think it can be fixed. How are you feeling about this? Do you feel safe?"

Shari smiled and said, "You know I am not scared. That's a pretty big step for me. Honestly, he has done some threatening stuff but he has never harmed me. It's just obnoxious and dreadful behavior. I think I am ready to just ignore it."

Mel nodded in understanding. "That's a great first step. Knowing you can't fix it and feeling like even if he does show up you have the skills to protect yourself makes a big change in confidence. I can see on your face that you are much less anxious."

Shari smiled and thought to herself, "I do feel better. Can I ask you some questions?" Mel nodded and leaned back in her chair. "Why is it that when I get upset by him it takes so long to calm down? I feel like it takes hours and should take more like minutes. I guess I am doing better because it's only hours now and not days, like it was."

Mel waited to see if she was done speaking and when Shari shrugged, Mel said, "You are correct, you are regulating yourself so much quicker now. I can see it myself. Noticing it yourself is also a good thing. You have to remind yourself that you were addicted to those fight-or-flight hormones and the love bombing hormones. Being in a relationship with someone who is as unpredictable as Tom is hard on your central nervous system. If you are surrounded by stress and fear all the time it's definitely challenging to learn to switch from anxious to calm. Even when you feel like you are more calm your nervous system can be on full alert. This raises cortisol levels, which can interfere with other hormones and even cause weight gain or loss. I am happy to see that you have not gained weight through this but many women do. Some gain weight, some lose and some find they have autoimmune symptoms or chronic pain from abusive situations. The longer you stay the more damaging it is to your physical body."

Shari's eyes got big and she asked, "You can become physically ill from trauma?"

Mel nodded. "It's more common than you think. Childhood trauma or not having the proper emotional growth as a child can leave you poorly regulated as an adult. Children are not meant to figure out all of their complex emotions on their own. A child with very communicative parents who makes the child feel comfortable discussing and expressing emotions in a healthy way is typically more emotionally balanced than a child who was left to try to understand the world on their own. Do you feel like you are in the first or second type of child?"

Shari chuckled. "My mother was explaining this to me a while back. I was definitely the child who thought I had to figure everything out on my own. I have always been extremely independent and would rather do things on my own."

Mel smiled and said, "I am not shocked. You spent a lot of time forming your emotional patterns. Unfortunately a child's mind is not advanced enough and they don't have enough real-world experience to be able to understand adult situations. You feeling like you had to protect your family from your dad is a trauma response. Being an overachiever and often very structured is commonly associated with that, too. Since you cannot control the things around you, your mind starts to make up stories to make sense of it all."

Shari nodded in agreement. "Yes, I can see how some of my behaviors were about controlling what I could. Being a straight-A student was within my control. Helping my mom with my siblings was also about control. This makes total sense."

Mel then said, "This all causes you to get stuck in the parasympathetic response to your surroundings—being on guard all the time. The cortisol and other hormones that are involved in this process can be addictive. Which means sometimes, even when there is no stress, your mind will create its own stress to get a hit of those hormones. Like a drug addict."

Shari's eyes got big. "You mean I am doing some of this to myself? I am causing myself to have more trauma?"

Mel nodded. "Do you sit around and think about things over and over and over again?"

Shari looked down. "Yes, especially when I'm trying to focus on something or sleep. I blame myself and rethink every detail. Oh, and I never put this together before but I usually feel really anxious or fidgety. Sometimes my heart feels like it's racing or beating way too hard. Is that all tied together?"

Mel nodded and smiled. "Yes, Shari. This is exactly what I am talking about. It's time for you to start calming down your nervous system so that you can rest before you begin to feel the physical effects of this constant state of panic."

Shari got a bit of a furrowed brow. Frowning, she said, "But how am I supposed to calm down when things keep happening?"

Mel leaned forward and said, "It's about regulating your nervous system in the times that you do have control so that when things are not in your control you have a faster recovery, and you don't dwell on it forever. We cannot control what other people do. I am here to tell you though that if you ignore him and do not give him the attention he wants he will get bored and move on to someone who will respond to his antics."

Mel looked intently at Shari and raised her eyebrows. "Are you ready to learn some tools to help calm down when you feel out of control?"

Shari could not help but get excited. She eagerly nodded and said, "Yes, I love doing these things. I want to be better. I want to live a normal life that's not filled with fear."

"Great," stated Mel. "I'll give you a couple of simple things you can do at home to start working on this phase of your healing journey. This form has a few exercises you can do. The first and easiest thing to do every day is gargle with some plain water for thirty seconds to a minute. This is an exercise you should do several times each day for a while. It helps tone the vagus nerve. Second, sing. I know it may sound silly but using your voice and the muscles that are necessary to control the voice when singing helps tone the vagus nerve too. This one is a little gross, but you can also gag yourself with your toothbrush on purpose. Have you noticed a lack of gag reflex?"

Shari thought for a minute and realized she could not remember the last time something made her gag. "I don't remember gagging at all for a long time. I mean, it's not something you think about. Should we gag often?"

Mel laughed and said, "Well hopefully you do not have a need to gag often but if you find that your gag reflex is not working it's a good sign your nervous system needs work. Some people have an oversensitive gag reflex too, but I find with trauma most often it's a lack of this reflex. You can just test it out while brushing your teeth. I know these exercises seem silly but they do work if you are consistent."

Shari nodded and looked at the clock. "Oops, I better go. I am so excited to start healing my nervous system. I'll see you Wednesday for group." Shari would never want to admit it but she looked forward to the group sessions. She loved being in the room with those amazing women. They made her feel strong. Shari walked back to her office with more confidence. She felt calm and reassured that things were going to get better and better.

21 HEALING

Shari had been using the exercises and really getting into singing in the car. She decided that she needed to sing some karaoke. She decided when she got home she was going to see if Lily wanted to go to the karaoke bar Thursday night. She assumed the answer would be yes and she was excited to practice more singing to help her body heal faster.

She got home from work and saw Leo had texted her while she was driving. She picked up the phone and read his message. "Hey Shari! I hope you are having a great day. My friend said he can buff out those scratches. Do you want me to come get the car and you can drive my truck tomorrow?"

Shari froze. Her mind started to race. What does this mean? What if I wreck his truck? Oh my. Then she stopped herself. "It doesn't mean anything and that's what insurance is for! Leo is just trying to help. Breathe. In five, four, three, two, one, pause, out five, four, three, two, one, again…"

She could feel herself calming. She decided to anchor herself in a childhood memory that was soothing. Grandma's fresh baked bread with butter. She could almost smell it and taste it. The soft bread was one of her favorite memories of her grandma's house. She could feel her heart rate slowing down. "Wow this stuff works!" she thought. "I never knew I could be so much in control of my own body before. This is fantastic." She looked back at the phone and replied, "If that is what you think will work best, I am fine with that."

She stuffed her phone into her purse and headed into the house. "I am healing." She smiled to herself and took in a deep breath of December air. She could taste a little smoke and it smelled like clean and crisp air with a hint of fireplace. "My favorite smell," she thought.

Leo replied to her message. "OK. I'll drop off the truck around eight if that works for you. It will be easier for me to drop off and pick up your car later in the day for you. I can always bring it to you at work if needed."

Shari thought to herself, "What a kind person." She replied, "That's great. Since you are coming over later should I make dinner?"

Leo was quick to reply. "I'd love dinner. See you around eight." Shari could not stop smiling. What a great day she was having.

Shari sped home from work. After slipping on something more comfortable She went to the pantry to see what she had to whip up a lovely dinner. It was going to be a good night.

Leo arrived a few minutes before eight o'clock and Lily had arrived just a little while before he did. Shari was still in the kitchen but had popped the cork on a bottle of wine. She looked at Leo and Lily and said, "Drinks, anyone?"

Leo motioned to the bag in his hand and said, "I brought some beer. That wine is too sweet for me."

Shari winked at him and nodded toward Lily. "More for us then. Dinner's almost ready. I hope you like lasagna. I made a big pan of it."

They sat down to eat the most lovely dinner. Shari's mom had taught her an amazing recipe for lasagna many years ago and it was sort of a signature dish for their family. Lily, Leo and Shari shared a wonderful meal and when the meal was completed they all got up to clean up the mess. Once the dishes were cleared Leo wiped off the table and said, "I hate to run but I better get home to bed. I have a big day tomorrow."

Shari smiled then stopped and said, "Wait, if messing with my car is causing you undue stress."

Leo stopped her with a kiss. "It's no bother. I am happy to help. I'll see you tomorrow. Hank said it would not take long at all to buff that out." He hugged Shari tightly, then turned to Lily and bowed and said, "Thanks for a lovely evening." They both laughed and Lily gave him a brief hug. She really hoped that Shari would connect with Leo. He seemed so perfect for her friend. He let himself out and waved a big goodbye and flashed one of his amazing smiles at Shari before closing the door behind him. Shari could not help but blush.

She finished cleaning up the kitchen while Lily looked through the TV for the news and suddenly her face went white. "Shari, come in here, you have to see this. It is shocking."

Shari moved from the sink to an angle that allowed her to see the TV while she dried her hands. "What is it?" she said.

"Apparently Tom got himself arrested. It looks like he finally got caught being abusive to the wrong person." Shari's heart started racing. OH NO, what if he blamed her for whatever this was. Shari was panicking. Then she heard Mel's voice in her head. *"This has nothing to do with you. You can't control it. You have to let it go."* She took a deep breath, let it out slowly and went back to her grandmother's kitchen again.

She was taking in the smells and thinking about the creamy butter and realized that her heart rate was slowing. "This really works, Lily! Mel taught me some tricks to balance my nerves and it's really effective. I am feeling so calm right now. Normally this would have set me back for days."

Lily jumped off the couch and hugged Shari. "I am so glad, Shari! This is fantastic news. I am so glad you found Mel. Hopefully Tom will be in jail for a while!"

Her first thought was, "I can't wait to tell Leo." She instantly blushed and Lily noticed.

"What? Why are you red-faced?"

Shari was a little embarrassed to admit it but she said quietly, "The first person I wanted to tell was Leo. Lily, I think I am falling for him. He's so kind and stable. He always does what he said he will do and he's just nothing like anyone I have ever dated before. None of them would have ever taken this long to get to know me. He never pressures me for sex. He's always a gentleman, even when he talks about work. He just has an air of confidence and calm about him. He never seems to get angry let alone show his temper. I mean he was angry about my car being damaged but he was so calm about it. I think you are right, Lily. He is a good guy."

Lily smiled at Shari and was almost moved to tears. "Welcome back, friend," she said softly. "I've missed you." Shari forgot all about the news. It didn't matter to her anymore. He had his own issues to deal with now and she was confident that he would no longer be a ghost in her dreams. She was ready to let go of the past and become the woman she was intended to be.

22 CHRISTMAS

Shari was so excited about Christmas this year. She had been having so much fun and she felt like she had purchased the perfect gifts for everyone she loved. Her mom had invited everyone to her home, including Leo's whole family. She was excited to see her sister and her family and to meet Leo's two brothers. They had been away at college but scheduled a special trip home for Christmas.

Rosalee's home was decorated beautifully. They had decided on gathering for Christmas Eve then going to midnight mass as a group. When Leo and Shari arrived her sisters' three beautiful children were playing outside in the yard. They screamed Aunt Shari as she climbed out of the truck. They all hugged her legs and immediately wanted to know who the man she was with was.

She introduced Leo to Sophie, Alex and Hannah as they climbed his legs and into his arms. Shari laughed and said "Well that didn't take long." Leo winked at her and put down the kids. "OK, let's help Aung Shari get all these presents into the house." All three kids yelled YAY and grabbed bags as Leo handed them out. The house smelled so amazing. Cinnamon, nutmeg, turkey and all the fixings were spread along the dining room table. It was a feast for sure.

Leo's family arrived just moments after they did so they went out to help carry in anything they needed help with. Leo's youngest brother Caleb swept Shari off her feet and spun her around with a big bear hug. "This must be the little lady I have heard so much about." He winked at her and waited for Leo to respond. "Yep," he said. "She's the one." Caleb looked at Shari and raised one of his perfectly trimmed eyebrows and said, "I thought I was gonna get a rise out of him for that comment." Shari chuckled and said, "Not today." She flashed him a big smile and said, "Where's this other brother I have heard so much about?" Lucas stepped out from behind the car and said "Oh, hi sorry, I was just grabbing these packages. He immediately put them down and hugged her. "It is so good to finally meet you. My parents can't stop talking about you!" Shari blushed and smiled at him and leaned in to help pick up some packages.

Shari made everyone a special eggnog recipe she had found and it was a big hit. They ate, laughed, opened presents and had an all around amazing family evening. It was so wonderful to have both of their families together. It was so nice to see her sister and their children too. She loved them so much and since she had those nightmares she had to admit she had been avoiding going to their house for a while. They just seemed so real. Now that Tom is in jail she hoped those nightmares would never come back.

Midnight mass was a big deal in their little town and seating was always a problem but in her moms larger town things were more laid back. There was plenty of room for all of them to sit near each other. The two families enjoyed a nice service with lots of cheer and Christmas carols.

As they were leaving. A man walked up to Shari and

wrapped his arms around her from behind. Picked her up off her feet and spun her around. Her first instinct was to panic. Who was this? Why were they touching her? What would Leo and his family think? She sprung into action and used her best self defense move on the unknown assailant. Her sharp and well trained elbow went into his ribcage with incredible force and when he dropped her she stomped on his foot and spun around to see a shocked face standing there. It was her friend Jerry, from work. He immediately apologized for startling her and then started laughing. "Man, you really took that self-defense class seriously," as he rubbed his sore ribs.

Shari was not so quick to recover. She felt her cheeks beginning to flush and her heart was racing. Her hands started to tremble and suddenly felt like she needed to sit. Leo, of course, recognized her symptoms immediately and gently grabbed her by the elbow and led her to a pew to have a seat. Jerry immediately ran to her side and knelt down to look her in the eyes. "Shari, I am so sorry. I never intended to startle you. I should have known better. Please forgive me?"

Shari took in a deep breath and nodded quietly. She could feel everyone staring at her which was not helping her calm down.

Rosalee and Angie sat down on each side of her. Angie whispered something to Leo and he immediately sprung into action. He quietly walked to the group of family and onlookers and asked them to please step outside. Once they were alone in the back of the church he walked back and sat in the pew in front of Shari so he could see her face. He could tell that she was recovering slowly. Jerry was still hovering and feeling awful for causing such a ruckus.

His wife was waiting for him in the back of the

church foyer. Her face showed obvious understanding of the situation. Jerry must have filled her in on Shari's history. Rosalee softly said, "Shari, deep breaths honey." Shari noticed as soon as she heard her say it that she had been holding her breath. She sucked in a deep ragged breath and let it out really slow. You could hear her shaking still in her breath. "That's it honey. You are safe." Shari dabbed a tear that had started to form at the corner of her eye and said, "I'm so sorry everyone. I feel like a drama queen!" Leo reached over and grabbed her hand and squeezed it. "Not a drama queen," he said softly.

Shari took in another deep breath and stood up. She gave Jerry a big hug and said, "I am so sorry if I hurt you. I was just so surprised. I went into panic mode." Jerry hugged his friend and kissed her cheek. "Shari, you do not owe me an apology. I should have known better than to walk up behind you like that. It was careless of me. You should have this gorgeous boyfriend of yours take me out back." He looked towards Leo and winked. "I'll leave you to your family. Merry Christmas Shari. I hope you have a wonderful Christmas with your family. I will see you at the office."

Jerry walked to the back of the church to collect his wife and arm in arm they walked out the big double doors. Shari looked at Leo and said, "I feel like an idiot. Can we go now?" She hugged the moms and Leo pulled her in close to his body. "Come on. Let's get you home."

As he was driving Leo was quietly watching Shari. Silently contemplating how he could help her feel better about what happened. After some time she looked at him with tears in her eyes and said, "I am so sorry." Leo glanced her way and said, "Why are you sorry? You didn't do anything." Shari shrugged and said, "Are you sure you want to be in a relationship with someone who panics and injures her friends? I am such a mess. You deserve a normal girlfriend and I am not normal! I feel like damaged goods."

Leo turned on the blinker and pulled off onto a side road and put the truck in park. He took off his seat belt and turned to face Shari. "You are not damaged goods. As a matter of fact I think you are an amazing human. You have been through an experience that most people would not understand. Personally I think you have handled the last year very well.

Here's how I see it. You chose to leave a bad situation. That alone must have been terrifying. You moved in with Lily and left many of your personal belongings behind. So many people would not have been able to accept that. You realized that you needed professional help and you got it! Not only have you worked on yourself, you have worked on your relationships with the people in your life and at work. I have watched you grow as a woman and I am so very proud of your progress."

Shari silently absorbed what he was saying and he patiently waited for her to reply. He could tell she was processing. She reached down and unbuckled herself, scooted over closer to him and leaned into his embrace. She took in a deep breath and appreciated his scent. He always smelled so good. She wrapped her fingers into his and just sat there for a few seconds to gather her thoughts. "Leo, thank you for that. I guess I don't give myself credit for what I have accomplished. I appreciate you noticing all of that and reminding me that I am on a journey. No man has ever given me the space to become anything. I have always been in relationships where I felt like I was in service to them. This whole process has been very eye opening. Thank you for being who you are."

Leo was happy to just sit and hold her tight. Right there on the side of the road in the dark. Shari looked up at

Leo and said, "I need some fresh air. Can we hop out of the truck for a minute before we drive the rest of the way home?" "Of Course. Let me get the door for you." Leo hopped out of the truck and ran around to Shari's side. He opened the door and lifted her to the ground and wrapped his arms around her for a big bear hug. The air was crisp and dry. They just stood there for a few minutes feeling the cold air on their skin.

Shari could feel the air burning her nostrils. Then she felt something on her eyelash. She blinked and leaned back and another snowflake fell and landed on her cheek. Leo saw the second one land and he immediately kissed it away, as if kissing away a tear. They both turned their heads to where the headlights were shining and they could see it was snowing and the flakes were huge. Like silver dollars falling from the sky. It was a beautiful scene to admire. It took literally seconds for Shari's hat to be covered in snow. She dusted her coat off and took a step toward the truck.

Leo said thoughtfully, "Would you like to come to my house tonight and stay? It's going to be really late when we get back." Shari smiled and nodded an emphatic yes. She knew Lily had a large family and she would probably be gone early in the morning anyway. Shari was excited to be with Leo for their first Christmas. They drove back to Leo's holding hands and singing carols together.

When they arrived at his house he went straight to the spare bedroom to make sure it was set up for Shari and she stopped him at the door. "I think I'll stay in your room tonight if that's ok?" Leo stopped and looked her square in the eye. "You know that you do not have to do that, right?" Shari nodded and smiled, "I know." Leo leaned down and in a single move, whisked her feet off the floor and carried her to the bedroom. He gently placed her on the bed and asked. "Do you need some pajamas?" Shari smiled and nodded. He grabbed her a big t-shirt and offered boxers or flannel pajama pants for her to sleep in. She opted for the pants and scurried off into the bathroom to change.

Leo fluffed her pillow and grabbed an extra blanket for the foot of the bed in case she got cold. They climbed into bed together for the first time since they had met. Shari rolled into his strong arms and laid her head on his chest. "Is this OK?" Leo kissed her forehead and said, "Perfect." In a flash they were both asleep.

Shari woke up to the sun peering through the windows. She could hear a fire crackling in the fireplace and movement in the kitchen. She got up and headed into the kitchen to see what was happening.

Leo was making breakfast. He had Christmas music playing and he was dancing around and singing into a spatula. "Well you're in a good mood this morning. Why didn't you wake me?" She winked at him and took the spatula so that she could sing a few bars. He grabbed her and hugged her with one of those famous bear hugs and spun her around. "You looked so peaceful and I wanted to start a fire so it would be cozy in here. I am so happy you stayed the night." Shari smiled and said, "Me too!"

He plopped a plate of eggs and bacon on the table and said, "Eat it while it's hot. I have a surprise for you after breakfast." Knowing fully that she could not wait for a surprise. Shari ran across the kitchen and said, "Surprise? What kind of surprise?" Leo laughed and said, "Not till you finish your breakfast." Shari scoffed and sat down and inhaled her breakfast. "OK, gone. Now tell me!"

Leo chuckled as he led her to the Christmas tree that they had decorated with the family at Thanksgiving. "There's one present left there. I think it has your name on it." Shari gasped and said, "Wait, you already gave me a gift. Why is there another one?" Leo smiled and hugged her and said, "This one is special." Shari flopped down to her knees in front of the tree and grabbed the box. She shook it, and smelled it and felt it like a little girl would. "What is it?" "Open it," Leo said with a smile.

Shari ripped open the box and found the most beautiful bottle of perfume she had ever seen. It was glass and very pretty. She instantly started spraying it so she could smell it. The aroma was so invigorating and sensual. "I love it!" she said and jumped up to hug his neck. "It smells so good and the bottle is so beautiful." "I just wanted to give you something personal that would make you feel beautiful." "Well, good job! I love it. Thank you so much." "It smells amazing on you," replied Leo.

They snuggled on the couch the rest of the day drinking hot chocolate, watching the snow and binged romantic Christmas holiday movies. Something Tom never would have agreed to. Shari felt truly blessed to be with Leo. Safe in his home and in his arms.

23 Moving on

Lily loved New Year's Eve and always planned a big celebration. This year she had reserved a table at a large hall where they went all out for the celebration. Decor, food, drinks with party hats and champagne at midnight. It was the event of the season and Shari and Lily were excited to shop for new dresses. They both found amazing gowns to wear for the event and they were so excited for the party.

Leo and Stan showed up right on time to pick them up for the night. They walked them to the car and slid them into the back seat like princesses.

At the event Leo walked Shari to the table and pulled out her chair so that she could sit. The decorations were breathtaking and everything was lit up. Stan looked over at Leo and motioned towards the bar. Leo nodded and bent down to kiss Shari on the cheek. "I'll be right back."

Shari and Lily were sitting at the table alone and watching all of the people enter the hall. Admiring their beautiful dresses and suits. Some men were even wearing tuxes. It was quite the event. Suddenly Lily gasped and pointed. Her mouth was wide open and no words were coming out. Shari slowly moved her eyes to what she was pointing at. Her mind was spinning. What was it? Who was it? Her heart started racing and she could feel beads of sweat popping up.

As her eyes landed on what Lily was pointing at, Shari burst into laughter. "What, Lily? It's ok." Lily opened her eyes even wider and said, "That woman is literally climbing Leo like a tree! Get over there and do something." Shari reached up and grabbed Lily's outstretched arm with one hand and gently pushed her chin up to close her gaping jaw. "Lily, if there is one thing I have learned in the last year it's this: I can't control what other people do. I trust Leo with my whole heart and I am not concerned about what she's doing. Leo can handle himself."

Lily gasped again and said sternly, "Well, if you aren't going to do something then I am!" She started to get up and Shari stood up next to her and said quietly. "No Lily. I would rather wait and see what he has to say about it. Give him a chance to handle this on his own." Lily plopped back into her chair with a scoff and a look of disgust on her face. "Fine, but I am watching her."

Leo and Stan made their way back to the table and gently sat their drinks down in front of the girls. Before Shari could even say anything Lily said bluntly, "Who was that tart?" Rolling her eyes and looking in the woman's direction. Leo burst into laughter. It's one of Caleb's ex-girlfriends. She's had a little too much to drink. For some reason she always thinks I am him when she's had a few drinks. I had to remind her that I am the taller and more good looking brother," he said with a smirk. "She says we look exactly the same from the back."

He looked at Shari to see how she was doing with this new information. She winked at him and took a sip of her drink. "You got that right!" she said with a smile.

Lily grabbed her by the arm and said let's go to the ladies

room. The two girls got up and walked towards the bathroom. Lily was still obviously upset about the incident "Why are you taking this so well? I would be pissed at them both. I can't believe you aren't in defense mode!" Shari put her arm around Lily's shoulders and said, "Honey, I am not at all worried about Leo. He is fully capable of handling her. Also, I am confident that if he didn't want to be with me he wouldn't. There's nothing I could do to change that. He knows what he wants and I am fully prepared to walk away if he begins to show signs of being like Tom. I don't think he will though. Don't worry about me. I'm paying attention."

Lily grumbled something under her breath and said, "I am proud of you for not ripping her hair out." Shari laughed and said, "That's the old me. She doesn't exist anymore. I am not fighting for anyone's affection. Come on, let's get those hotties out on the dance floor." They ran back to the table and grabbed Leo and Stan and headed towards the dance floor. Leo whispered in Shari's ear, "You ok?" Shari nodded and said, "Never better." Leo hugged her and said, "Good, you know I would never." Shari cut him off and said, "Yes, I know. Let's dance!"

The rest of the night was magical. There were friends, and hugs and laughter. Everyone danced until they were exhausted. Leo sat down at the table with Stan and watched as Lily and Shari danced to an old song they loved. Shari looked his way and smiled. She admired his gentle ways and how easy it was to get along with him. Sure she did feel a tiny pang of jealousy when that girl was all over him but she knew it wasn't her place to handle it. She was so proud of Leo for how he did. "I am growing." She thought to herself with a smile.

Midnight arrived too soon. The girls were having so much fun dancing that Leo and Stan had to come out to the dance floor to give them their party favors. Shari slipped on a headband with sparkles and chose a noise maker she could spin. Leo donned a top hat and a whistle. Together they all counted down ten, nine, eight, seven, six, five, four, three, two, one. "Happy New Year!" Leo's lips landed on Shari's with a smile. He lifted her off her feet and whispered in her ear. "You know they say what you are doing at midnight on New Years is what you will be doing all year." Shari leaned back and smiled and laid a big kiss on his lips then said, "Good, because I want to be kissing you all year!" Leo laughed and said, "Me too!" The music started up again and they all danced. It was a night to remember for sure.

Shari leaned in to Leo and looked towards Stan and Lily and said, "You think they will be together next year?" Leo smiled and shrugged his shoulders. "Only time will tell, but I'm here to tell you that Stan is smitten with Lily. She's going to have to throw rocks at him to get him to leave." They both laughed and Shari said, "Well, She's done worse! I really like Stan. I hope they stay together. I love our group so much."

After the dance Leo and Stan wicked the girls into the back seat and headed towards Lily's house. Shari invited them both in for a night cap and a snack which they both agreed to. After a while Lily and Stan wandered off towards her bedroom and Shari looked at Leo and said, "You gonna stay?" "Only if you want me to," he said kindly. She winked and said, "Oh, I do."

She grabbed his hand and headed towards her bedroom. Leo jokingly said, "I don't have any pajamas and I don't think yours will fit me." Shari closed the door behind them and said, "I don't think you are going to need them tonight," with a grin. She wrapped her arms around his neck and planted her lips firmly on his. "There's something else I want to be doing this year that we haven't done yet," She whispered in his ear. Leo smiled and swept her off her feet and onto the bed. "If you are sure," he said softly. Shari smiled and said firmly, "I'm so sure!"

The next morning Leo rolled over and wrapped his arms around Shari. He was a little concerned that she may have done something she wasn't quite ready for and he wanted to make sure she was ok.

She snuggled in closer and whispered, "Happy New Year, Leo." He kissed the top of her head and asked, "Are you happy?" She rolled over and kissed him full on the lips and said, "I've never been happier." He sighed and hugged her tightly. He felt so overwhelmed with her beauty and presence. He could not help but think to himself. "I think this is the girl I am going to marry, someday." He then pushed the thought aside because he knew she would not be ready for that kind of discussion yet. "Someday," he thought, "someday."

Lily knocked on the door and said, "Y'all ready for some breakfast? I am starving." Shari answered with excitement, "Yes! We will be right out." They jumped up and got dressed and headed out to the kitchen where Lily and Stan were sipping on some hot coffee. "Man what a fun night!" Lily said with a snicker. "Did you two have fun?" She was doing that I see you motion with her fingers. Holding two fingers to her eyes then pointing at Shari. Leo could tell what she was getting at and laughed, "I'll never tell." He winked at Lily and went to grab their coats.

Lily grabbed Shari and whispered to her, "You finally? What? New Years? OMG! This is huge." Shari smiled and nodded at her. "They say what you are doing on New Years will be done all year long. I figured it was a good time to start planning my year!" She laughed out loud and elbowed Lily. The two of them hugged and Lily whispered in her ear, "I am so happy for you. I hope this is the best year ever"

The next few weeks would be a whirlwind of business. A new year, new relationship and exciting beginnings sounded pretty good to Shari.

23 LOVE

Shari stepped out of Lily's house and walked toward the car. It was a beautiful day. The sun was shining and the air felt humid. Spring was Shari's second favorite season. It was full of new beginnings. Changing the gray winter trees to green and encouraging the flowers to bloom Spring was always a beautiful time of the year.

She had not heard one peep out of Tom in months. She had no idea where he was or what he was up to and that suited her just fine. Work was busy. Life was calm. Shari was happy.

She called Leo on the way to work and asked him what he was doing for lunch. She rarely ever asked him to do anything and she thought he might appreciate her taking the initiative to ask him out for once. He was always making the plans and she felt like it would be good of her to show her appreciation. She could hear the smile in his voice when he answered. "Good morning, beautiful. How are you today?"

Shari blushed and smiled to herself. "Why am I blushing alone in my car?" She decided it was because it was Leo. They had become so close over the last few months. She answered, "I am great. How are you?" "I am great, too." he said. Shari replied, "I was just wondering if you wanted to meet for lunch today?"

"Of course I do," he said with a chuckle. "Want me to pick you up at the office about noon? I have to be over that way for a job today."

Shari, knowing it meant a lot to him to be able to pick her up and not meet her somewhere, said, "I'd love for you to pick me up." She loved being able to accommodate his love language. He was big into acts of service for others and she had to admit she appreciated his desire to serve.

Walking across the parking lot she was taking in the morning air. "What a beautiful spring day," she said to herself out loud. As she opened the door to the back staircase she noticed the bulb was out. She reached into her purse and grabbed her phone for a flashlight, turned it on and went right up the stairs without even a twinge of the panic she had felt last year when the door locked behind her. She noted her calm demeanor and sent up a little gratitude for her journey. She was not the same person she was a year ago and she had not had a panic since Christmas Eve. She chuckled to herself. "I should ask Jerry how his ribs are doing."

She had received a promotion at work that allowed her to afford her own place, but she was so happy at Lily's she decided to just start a nest egg for something later. It felt good to be self-reliant and so much more emotionally regulated. She rarely ever had any issues with her heart racing and if it did start she was able to easily calm it down using the tools she had at her disposal.

She had learned so much from her friends and Mel. The ladies in the group were also so inspiring. She had stopped one-on-one appointments with Mel but continued going to group because she loved mentoring others. Being there to show the women in her group that recovery from abuse is possible and not all abuse looks the same made her feel so fulfilled.

Of the most important things she had learned over the last year was that she was responsible for her own happiness. She had learned to set boundaries that helped her feel safe and confident. She also was in such a beautiful relationship with Leo, Lily and her family. Life was becoming blissful and she was ready for all that entailed. She sat down at her desk and smiled at the fresh roses she had received the day before from Leo. She opened the card again and read the caption out loud. "Just because." She silently smiled and tucked the card into her top drawer. She had a collection of them and each was just as important to her as the others.

Leo arrived for lunch and called her cell to let her know he was in the parking lot. She picked up her purse and headed for the door. Susan peeked around the edge of her cubicle and said with a wink, "Hot date?"

Shari blushed and replied, "The hottest. I'll be back in about an hour."

As usual, Leo was waiting for her with the passenger-side door open. She climbed in and he kissed her cheek and closed the door. Hopping in the driver's seat and fastening his seat belt he looked at Shari and said, "Where to?"

She smiled and said, "Let's go to our favorite sandwich place if that's good for you."

Leo nodded with a smile and dropped the truck into drive. "I love going there, Shari. It always reminds me of our first lunch together." Shari smiled and said, "Me too."

Shari had blossomed over the last few months and she was feeling more safe and confident. She had been able to open up more and she had learned to trust Leo so much. She loved him and wasn't afraid to show it. She smiled adoringly at him as he drove. She loved his tousled hair, his big brown eyes and his chiseled features. He was truly a good-looking man but what was most important to Shari was his heart. It was big and he was so solid. She had to turn her smile to the window as a thought crossed her mind. "I think I could marry this man." It wasn't a thought she had willingly allowed before. She had been so against marriage because of the damage relationships had on her in the past. She felt confident in her ability to see him for exactly who he was though. He didn't seem to have any secrets.

His family loved her and his mom kept hinting that she was waiting on grandchildren, which just made Shari laugh. She was in no hurry but loved watching Leo squirm when she said it. She also loved having his family in her world. They were all so kind and thoughtful. She could see them being wonderful grandparents. "That was a new thought!" She silently laughed at herself.

She looked at Leo lovingly. She was well aware that she had not been through this healing journey alone and she knew it was a necessary part of her own emotional development. She was so thankful for her journey. Even though it was a rough ride for a while it had opened her eyes to so many things. Feeling confident and fulfilled was all that she had ever wanted. She also noted that because of her experience she would be able to pass on her understanding to her children, which made her feel so proud of how far she had come.

As Leo pulled the truck into a parking spot near the building and walked around to open her door, she waited. She had learned to appreciate his desire to keep her safe and the high level of respect he had for her and all people.

As she slid out of the seat onto the ground in front of him he leaned down and kissed her cheek and whispered,

"I hope you know that I love you."

Shari leaned into him and hugged him tightly. She took in the smell of his shirt and how strong his arms felt around her. She loved him so much but he had never said it before and she wasn't sure if it was time yet or not. She was so relieved to hear those words. Shari looked up at him and as a tear slid down her cheek she said those three little words for the first time in such a very long time. "I love you." This time she knew it was real.

EPILOGUE

Shari woke with a startle. Did she hear something? The sun was up and clearly it was going to be a beautiful day. She grabbed her robe from the chair next to the bed and quickly walked down the hallway towards the kitchen. Everything seemed to be in place there. She opened the door to the garage and the only thing there was her car. She listened intently for another noise but heard nothing.

She decided it must have been a dream and headed back towards the bedroom. She paused briefly to look at the photos in the hallway. It was hard to believe that she already had grandchildren. She lovingly looked at the photos and embraced the comforting memories over the years.

Her favorite photo of all was then from her wedding day. She smiled as she touched the frame. A tear slipped down her cheek and she smiled remembering how wonderful that day was. It was hard to believe it was 30 years ago already.

She decided to get out the photo album and take a walk down memory lane. She sat comfortably in the large chair by the bed and covered her feet with a comforter.

One by one she looked through the images. Smiling at some and feeling sorrow for some. She missed her father desperately. He had passed away just a year before. She missed their talks and his wisdom. She laughed to see a picture of him and Rosalee together. They tried so hard to let everyone believe they were not seeing each other secretly for years. They never remarried but they were always together. She laughed softly and said to herself "Whatever works."

She remembered the nightmares she had when she had first left Tom. They were so real. It seemed like a lifetime ago and she stopped for a moment to feel gratitude for her journey. Without what happened with Tom she wasn't sure that her life would have turned out so amazing. She silently thanked him and God for the opportunity to have those experiences. Even though they were traumatic. They formed the person she was to become in such an amazing way.

She no longer felt anger towards him. She understood that her emotional growth needed a starting point and their break up was the catalyst that helped her become the woman she was today.

She found a picture of that New Years Eve when the four of them had gone to the big event. What a beautiful night that was. It was the first time she really felt like her and Leo might have a real future together. They all looked so gorgeous in their party attire.

She laughed at an image of Lily, Stan and their kids from many years ago. They always sent the best Christmas cards. They had four amazing children who were always at Shari's house. Their children had all grown up together and she was like their second mom. They even called her Aunt Shari.

There was even a photo of her and her mom from

that day they spent at the B & B. "Wow!" She thought to herself. "That was a completely different person than I am today. I learned so much from my mom. How to recognize generational patterns or any patterns for that matter. How to calm myself when I was stressed, how to communicate my needs and feelings with others. What gaslighting and love bombing were and how to spot a true relationship with a healthy partner. Knowledge that I took the time to pass on to my nieces and nephews as well as my own children."

The most important information she recalled from that time was that cortisol and love hormones are addictive. She remembered being shocked that she was creating her own drama just to get a hit of those hormones when she was feeling low. It was a challenge to break that habit. She recalled that finding other ways to raise the right hormones with exercise and hobbies that she enjoyed made such a clear difference in her emotional stability.

She was so glad that she had learned so much about human behavior and communicating her feelings. She felt like she had done a really good job of communicating with her loved ones over the last thirty years. She felt like she lived a very fulfilling life. She still went to group a few times a year just to be supportive of others. It was a little shocking that things seemed to never change for some people. They lived the same patterns over and over again.

Shari closed the book with a smile, stood up to head to the shower and heard the garage door start to open. Aww, he's home. She made her way to the kitchen to give her beloved husband a hug and a kiss before she started her day. Life was truly magical, and she was fully grateful for having the opportunity to live it.

The Ties That Bind

ABOUT THE AUTHOR

Annette Copeland's journey, from a small town in mid-Missouri to a life of exploration and self-discovery, is as captivating as it is inspiring. Leaving home at the tender age of sixteen to embark on a path of early marriage and motherhood, Annette's experiences have been nothing short of a rollercoaster of transformation and growth.

Single motherhood taught her resilience and determination. Embracing these qualities, Annette pursued her passion for natural health, becoming a naturopathic doctor. This career took her on a journey across North America, exploring diverse cultures and landscapes, enriching her life and broadening her perspective.

In 2020, Annette returned to Southern Missouri, a full circle moment that brought her back to her roots and reignited a long-held dream. It was here that she decided to complete a project that began in 2006 – this very book.

Annette's writing is imbued with the insights gained from her own life experiences. She is deeply passionate about helping others realize their full potential, advocating for emotional intelligence, and breaking free from the shackles of toxic and abusive behaviors. Her work is a mission to empower individuals, guiding them to shed the burdens of generational shame and guilt and embrace their true selves.

You can follow Annette on Instagram @askdrannette or find her on Facebook as Annette Copeland, ND. Visit her website at AnnetteCopeland.com.

The Ties That Bind

If you or someone you love is being abused please don't stay silent. They might not even be aware that what they are experiencing is abuse. Many relationships can be healed through therapy, but some cannot.

If you're hesitating—telling yourself that it's none of your business, you might be wrong, or that the person might not want to talk about it—keep in mind that expressing your concern will let the person know that you care and may even save their life.

Talk to the person in private and let them know that you're concerned. Point out the signs you've noticed that worry you. Tell the person that you're there for them, whenever they feel ready to talk. Reassure them that you'll keep whatever is said between the two of you, and let them know that you'll help in any way you can.

Remember, abusers are very good at controlling and manipulating their victims. People who have been emotionally or physically abused are often depressed, drained, scared, ashamed, and confused. They need help getting out of the situation, yet their partner has often isolated them from their family and friends.

I highly recommend that they do not confront their abuser until they have a plan in place to escape the situation if needed. Abusers do not like being called out on their behavior and it can create a potentially dangerous situation.

For nationwide resources in the US
https://www.thehotline.org/ or 1-800-799-7233